Memories of Kentish

The Rivers Cray & Darent

Alan Stoyel

A nostalgic look at the watermills of two much-changed rivers over 50 years ago

Landmark Publishing

Published by

Landmark Publishing

The Oaks, Moor Farm Road West, Ashbourne, DE6 1HD
Tel: (01335) 347349 Fax: (01335) 347303
Email: landmark@clara.net Web: www.landmarkpublishing.co.uk

1st Edition
13 ISBN: 978-1-84306-418-3

Print: Cromwell Press
Design by: Michelle Prost

Front Cover: An illustration of Elm View Mill, Westerham in its working days
Back Cover: Whitley Mill, Chevening
Page 3: Brasted Mill

Memories of Kentish Watermills
The Rivers Cray & Darent

Alan Stoyel

A nostalgic look at the watermills of two much-changed rivers over 50 years ago

Landmark Publishing

Contents

Preface

My first memory of a watermil was when, at the age of eight, I sat with my father on a wall beside the tailrace of Longford Mill, near Dunton Green, and we each sketched the mill. I was fascinated by the broad, overshot waterwheel beneath the building. Little did I know the long-term effect that view would have on me. Over the following 35 years this mill lost its character in a series of dramatic changes, all deeply regretted, until it was finally removed completely, leaving no trace. Yet I still had my memories, and an awful sketch!

Lucky enough to be born a Kentish man in 1939, I was growing up at a time when so much was waiting to be discovered and investigated. There were still old men who had worked in and around watermills, and who were pleased to explain and reminisce about their past way of life. Owners and tenants alike would welcome a schoolboy who had a passionate interest in what may have seemed common-place to them, and they would patiently permit freedom of access. In general, despite living fairly close to London, mine was still a rural environment. Everything was more relaxed, and cycling was still a pleasure. It was a different world.

The Darent has a particular place in my heart because it was Elm View Mill on the outskirts of Westerham that was the subject of my first attempt at understanding a watermill. I was 13 at the time, and I had cycled to this ruined mill about twelve miles from home. It still had its waterwheel, and I learnt to admire how the clear water of such a small stream had been harnessed to drive heavy machinery. There was no ugliness, no pollution. The building had become a ruin, and was returning to nature, with a result that was, to me, an improvement on anything that nature alone could have produced. In addition, the history of the place, and the contrast between its present serenity and its industrial past, was extraordinary and hypnotic.

Soon I decided to follow the river Darent downstream from Westerham, and the next mill I came to was at Brasted. This mill had lost its waterwheel and

Alan Stoyel (©John Teale)

machinery, and the millpond had been filled in, but the owner took me to where the wheel had been, and even showed me an old glass negative of the mill showing the waterwheel in place. When he saw how excited I was, he said I could keep the negative. My future was now becoming clear. There was no turning back!

From then on I investigated other parts of the Darent valley, looking at the site of every mill I could find, talking to anyone I met who looked as if they might be able to give me some information. For my fourteenth birthday I was given a box-camera, which opened up more exciting possibilities. Every site had something of note, and every mill was different. A fascinating and absorbing study was gaining momentum, and the quest for "one more mill" was firmly established.

A vital aspect of my good fortune was my parents.

They would cycle out in search of a suitable subject, such as a church or other historic building, or a landscape with character, and then sketch it. They instilled in me an appreciation of details of rural life and of natural history, and a love and respect for what had been achieved in the past. My father Derek was a well-known expert and recorder of industrial and road steam locomotives, so I was also privy to a contrasting and totally fascinating world of smoke, grease, and old engines. My mother, too, had a very general interest in windmills. My love of things old and mechanical was a logical outcome. When I developed my passion for water-powered mills and machinery my parents viewed it positively, treated it as a natural progression, and gave me every encouragement. A year's subscription to the Wind and Watermill Section of the Society for the Protection of Ancient Buildings was an inspired Christmas present to this particular 14 year-old! Despite steam still taking pride of place, for the rest of his life my father shared my interest, accompanying me on many visits, taking photographs and notes, finding references and typing out extracts. His excellent photographs feature conspicuously in this book.

My father's connection with the world of agricultural steam engines was sometimes extremely useful. When I was 15, I was welcomed by John Russell of Cranbrook, who knew my father quite well. He gave me a detailed guided tour of his wonderful windmill, and entertained me with reminiscences and facts about some of his local watermills. Peter Davies of Cheriton was a correspondent of my father's, and, in the same year, he took us both round the amazing Horn Street Mill, near Cheriton where he lived, shortly before it was demolished. These were unforgettable experiences, and I never tired of listening, making notes of what such knowledgeable old people had to say.

I had become conscious of the way life had changed over the course of the previous generation. I was determined to make as much use as possible of reminiscences of old people who had seen, or had some association with, mills which had either changed their character or had gone completely. Here was unique information, freely available, about a fascinating, yet unrecorded subject. As I talked to these elderly people it became clear how privileged I was to have their memories to add flesh to the bones of what remained of these Kentish mills. Mr Nicholas of Westerham, for example, then a wonderful old man of 99, was able to give me information about his local Elm View Mill even going right back to when he was 14, the same age as I was, in 1868!

In the 1950s, when my study of watermills really took hold, many people were taking an interest in steam engines, but nobody seemed to be taking any notice of the exciting watermills which were gradually disappearing from the Kent landscape. A sense of urgency was driving me to record as much as I could of what still survived.

In 1961 I moved right away, to Canada, living in an extraordinarily contrasting world, working in mines for gold and for copper, but I have never lost my appreciation for the extra dimension the Kent watermills have given to my life. These were indeed formative years, and they have helped enormously in recording watermills elsewhere – a study which has occupied so much of my life. With the recent Kent initiative which has been spear-headed by the Mills Archive Trust, now seems a unique opportunity for me to draw together some of my Kentish observations and records, most of

Introduction

This book is totally subjective. It pulls together the bones of what I recorded in and around some of the Kentish watermills in my youth. It features an area under siege, part of it disappearing beneath the insatiable pressure of the advancing metropolis. Some of what was still Kent at that time has now been officially commandeered by London. I have used my field observations from the 1950s, with contemporary photographs taken by my father and by me, together with gathered oral, written and pictorial information. Later visits have sometimes been made, recording many sad changes. Some of these visits have been used, where relevant, to illustrate what has gone. A picture is thus painted of the final stage in the disappearance of rural milling; a mixture of sadness at the loss of so much that was rural, attractive and full of interest, and gratitude for what I have been privileged to experience. Although I have done some documentary research, such material has only been included here where it is felt to be relevant in what is essentially a personal record of nostalgia from over 50 years ago.

Acknowledgements

Firstly I should like to acknowledge all those who shared their knowledge and memories with me, and those who welcomed me to their properties all those years ago. I never knew the names of many, but virtually all of them will have gone by now. To some I owe a special debt of gratitude in such formative years of my life. There were my parents, Derek and Winnie Stoyel, who were so supportive of my passion, particularly my father, who not only came to share my interest, but carried out independent research and took many photographs.

Others who encouraged a teenager in his quest included Mr. Brealey of Sundridge, Monica Dance (the Secretary of the Society for the Protection of Ancient Buildings), Peter Davies of Cheriton, E. Hammond of Orpington, Walter Millen of Horton Kirby, Mr. Nicholas of Westerham, John Russell of Cranbrook, H.E.S. Simmons of Shoreham-on-Sea, my uncle Anthony Stoyel of Otford, Philip Street of Sidcup, Donald Strickland of Dartford and Mr. V. H. Thompson of Sutton at Hone. Thanks are also due to Rob Cumming for subsequent information, to the National Monuments Record for permission to use a photograph from the collection, and to John Teale for the photograph in the preface.

I would like to thank the Mills Archive Trust, and also Lindsey Porter of Landmark Publishing Limited for his help in bringing this publication together. I am especially grateful to Critchell Britten for her encouragement, helpful criticism and patience.

The River Cray

Orpington Mill. The mill and house across the pond; Mr. Harrild, c.late 1890s.

A view of the mill and house, looking across the lower of a pair of spring-fed ponds. The photograph shows the extension to the left for the steam engine, with the chimney, known as "Colgate's Folly", behind it. This tranquil scene lasted until the 1930s, when the pond was in-filled and the whole area was redeveloped for housing. Today no trace of the mill remains.

Fed from springs in the Upper Chalk, the Cray flows over much more recent gravels in a broad valley of restricted topographic expression. The river becomes tidal immediately below its lowest mill, and, within a mile, forms a tributary of the tidal River Darent just north of Dartford. The Cray had long been an important source of power for a variety of industries. Along its 7½ miles course, it used to drive more than 15 waterwheels. As far as is known, none of the mills on this river had a turbine installed. The available power, together with the quality of the water, combined to support three main industries – papermaking, flour production and textile printing. However, water abstraction for the fast-growing suburban sprawl had depleted the flow of the clear chalk stream running into the London basin to an enormous degree. The volume of water it was carrying in my youth was nothing compared with what must have been the case a century before. Ironically this abstraction was happening at the very time that there was an unprecedented demand for the products of the mills which the stream had powered. Nowhere were such pressures more acute than with the River Cray.

Those mills which survived installed steam engines for extra power, but coal was expensive. A couple of them fought back with modernisation, using steel rollers instead of the traditional millstones. In the meantime one of the most entrepreneurial of the local millers set a new trend in 1891 with the huge expansion of a new steam-powered roller mill on the dockside at Erith, north of Dartford. Here ships could unload their cargoes of relatively cheap wheat on the premises, and the bulk flour could be distributed by road and rail. Against such economies of scale no traditional watermill could possibly compete.

Featured here are 13 mill sites on the Cray. Of the 5 corn mills, 3 had disappeared before I was born and the other 2 have gone since I began my investigations. The 4 paper mills, too, have all gone, 2 of these long before my time. For the 4 fabric printing works even the former use of water for power can only be surmised in a couple of cases, and not one of the works survives now. The relentless disappearance of the mills has been depressing and wholesale, as has the character of this, once rural, valley. The whole course of the river has now been absorbed into the area of Greater London.

Orpington Mill (See also pages 9 & 11-13)

Orpington Mill, virtually at the source of the River Cray, was served by ponds fed by chalk springs. Despite being at the head of the river, it appears to have once had three pairs of millstones, a testimony to the volume of water produced by these springs. It was a traditional weather-boarded building with an overshot waterwheel of about 11 feet 6 inches diameter by 9 feet wide.[2] As might be anticipated, scarcity of water must have been a problem at times, and there was a tall, square brick chimney stack for a steam engine. This stack was sometimes referred to locally as "Colgate's Folly", after John Colgate, who was the miller there from the 1840s until the early 1870s. Apparently this was so called because it did not function as well as it should.[3] The mill complex became a casualty to building development, and was demolished in 1934-5.[4] Its rural surroundings, including the large pond, were to disappear completely beneath a housing estate.

Needless to say, I never saw the mill, but I compared old and present-day maps, trying to locate under which house or garden it would have been. The stream was enclosed in a long concrete culvert, emerging several hundred yards further north. On one occasion I ventured up this as far as I dared, walking, then stooping, and finally having to crawl in the water as the tunnel reduced in size. I was keen to find some tangible evidence of the elusive mill that had been so wantonly destroyed, so close to

where I lived. In my mind, somewhere down there some fragment of ancient masonry could possibly still survive. Not surprisingly, all was in vain; the only result was a soaking, and two extremely bruised knees.

One day an old man came to the house to see my father. His name was Philip Street, and he was the grandson of the eminent architect George Street (1824-1881). Unfortunately he was both deaf and dumb, but he was accompanied by a lady who was able to interpret for him and speak on his behalf. He was very interested in old buildings and used to make detailed notes on those which were being demolished at the time, either because of war damage, or from mere dereliction. When he learnt of my interest in watermills he promised me some information about Orpington Mill. Sometime later he returned with some notes, and gave me some beautiful internal and external photographs of the mill which he had taken twenty years before. His copious notes were hand-written on individual sheets of paper, about three inches square, stacked between two pieces of cardboard, and fastened with a rubber band. Through the kindness of both Mr. Street and my father, the notes were duly borrowed and converted into seventeen pages of typed text. By this amazing turn of events I now had a detailed written record of the mill, demolished over twenty years before, and Mr. Street's photographs became some of my most treasured possessions.

Opposite bottom: Orpington Mill. The mill loft; Philip Street, 4th July 1934.

Looking along the central walkway which ran the length of the mill. Despite demolition being imminent, the general structural condition looks excellent. The pulley at the top of the photograph would have carried the chain for hoisting the grain. The sacks of corn would have been hoisted through hinged trap-doors. These are visible, with one of the doors flapped back, at the bottom margin of the picture. The sacks would then have had their contents tipped into the deep bins each side of the walkway. From here the corn was fed down to the millstones, and any other machines, by gravity.

Orpington Mill. The mill and house; photographer unknown, c.1890s.

A view of the front of the range of buildings. The edge of the pond is visible behind the lamp-post, and the top of the steam engine chimney can be seen over the mill roof. The young man is likely to have been one of the Hodsoll family, who were the millers here at the time. The stable-door to the left of the wagon enters the mill at stone-floor level, and would have been used to take corn into the mill. The meal floor of the building, where the products were weighed and despatched, was below this level, and was only accessible from the yard on the downstream side of the mill. An old millstone stands against the wall beyond the door; this marks where a tunnel led the water in to drive the water-wheel. The lack of windows above stone-floor level is because this part of the building consisted of massive bins for the storage of corn.

Orpington Mill. The stone-floor; Philip Street, 4th July 1934.

A fine view of the middle one of the three storeys, showing two pairs of millstones which are in their working positions, but lacking their wooden stone furniture. The millstones were driven by machinery on the meal floor below. The massive 18th century, 16-sided upright shaft extends up into this floor where, at its top, it carries an iron crown-wheel with wooden cogs. This drove a series of horizontal shafts with belt-wheels, seen in the picture, connecting to the sack-hoist and all the other ancillary machines. The iron crown-wheel had superseded the original wooden one, but the blocked mortice for one of the wooden arms is just visible in the upper-most part of the upright shaft. The waterwheel was situated beneath the roughly-floored area beyond the upright shaft. The words "ORPINGTON MILL" can be seen stencilled onto a chute, made out of old flour sacks on the right-hand margin of the photograph.

Orpington Mill. The waterwheel; Philip Street, 4th July 1934.

The internal overshot waterwheel is completely of iron and has a certain amount of lime-scale, built up over the years from the hard chalk-fed water. The wheel has closely-spaced buckets – suggestive of a limited water supply. The purpose of the iron bevel ring gear on the wheel is not clear. Presumably it drove a pump, or some other machine unconnected with milling, but it does not appear to have suffered a great deal of wear. It is too light in construction to have been the connection to the steam engine. The circular iron wheel-shaft is fitted with heavy hexagonal bosses where each of the three sets of arms is supported. This suggests the waterwheel was originally fitted on a wooden shaft. The main machinery to drive the millstones is on the far side of the waterwheel, behind the corrugated iron sheeting. Mr. Street noted that the wallower and spur-wheel were both of iron, which indicates they were 19th century replacements.

Snelling's Mill, St. Mary Cray. Mill and house, photographer unknown, 1880s.

A photograph, kindly given by Arthur Eldridge, showing the mill and the adjoining house, each of two phases, and both with mansard roofs; an unusual combination. The 18th century core of small mill and house had been extended outwards in two directions in the early 19th century to produce this very attractive group. By the turn of the century all had gone, except for the waterwheel, which was spared. Now, however, there is hardly even a trace of where this mill once stood.

Snelling's Mill, St. Mary Cray. Pumphouse interior, Alan Stoyel, 10th January 1960.

The waterwheel of the demolished corn mill was used for pumping water. The pump was in a corrugated-iron shed on a brick base. This photograph is inside the shed and shows the lower part of a beam pump with its cast-iron supporting frame. Behind it is the spur-geared iron wheel with wooden cogs which drove the pump. This wheel is on the iron wheel-shaft, and the arms of the waterwheel can be glimpsed through a hole in the corrugated-iron.

Snelling's Mill, St. Mary Cray

(See also page 14)

The next mill downstream was Snelling's Mill, St. Mary Cray. This was once a corn mill, but it had ceased work long ago and was demolished in about 1885.[5] Once again Philip Street came up with two excellent external pictures, which he had copied, of the mill and house. The mill was a long building, mainly of brick, with two storeys below a deep mansard tiled roof. The adjoining house was a double-range building, one range in brick, the other weatherboarded. The whole site had been cleared long ago, except for the waterwheel.

In the 1950s the iron waterwheel and a fine iron beam-pump in a corrugated iron shed were still complete and in reasonable condition, despite an enveloping cover of thick ivy. It was in 1956 that I tried to record the remains, with measurements and photographs. By then I was fairly familiar with waterwheels, but a beam–pump was something that was both foreign to me and of much less interest. Later, of course, I greatly regretted that I had not paid more attention to this unusual survival.

The machinery had been pumping water to fountains and conservatories at "The Rookery",[6] a large brick house on the east side of the nearby road. The wheel was likely to have been the one that had powered the corn mill. It was breast-shot, completely of iron, 13ft 4ins diameter and 8ft 6ins wide, with three sets of arms on a circular iron shaft. The 56 iron buckets were sharply curved, held by plain, cast-iron shrouds with no visible inscription. At that stage the wheel's condition seemed to be very good.

In 1962 the ivy was stripped off, exposing the whole wheel and shed, but this immediately led to attacks of vandalism and, by December of that year, part of the wheel had been smashed and removed. The whole area was eventually cleared by Orpington Urban District Council, sometime between April 1963 and March 1964. My next site visit was in September 1975, by which time the wheel-race had been rebuilt in the form of an ornamental cascade. Some scratch-marks, still visible on the brickwork, were all that remained to show where this powerful wheel had been. Thirty years later I returned to find the area had undergone yet another transformation. It had become a public park, and not a trace could be seen of where the mill had stood.

Snelling's Mill, St. Mary Cray. Waterwheel; Alan Stoyel, 24th December 1962.

The waterwheel had survived, along with its corrugated- iron pump-house, until it was vandalised in 1962. The partly-smashed, completely iron wheel shows its construction to advantage, with the three sets of arms, and the form of the buckets. That it is a breast wheel can be seen clearly, with the water entry at shaft level. In contrast to the waterwheel at Orpington Mill, here the iron casting comprising the arms is of the same age as the iron wheel-shaft.

The River Cray at St. Mary Cray. Derek Stoyel, 24th December 1958

A view of the embanked river, looking downstream, from close to where the Upper Paper Mill once stood. Beyond the railway viaduct can be seen part of Joynson's Paper Mill to the left, and the roof of the parish church to the right. The water which once drove a waterwheel at the upper site has been carried on at its high level to the lower mill, thus increasing the head, and thus the power, available there.

Joynson's Paper Mill, St. Mary Cray. Derek Stoyel, 14th December 1957

The leat, known locally as "the iron river", running into the paper mills complex. This was the head-race for the waterwheel, with the main stream running at a much lower level, just to the right of the narrow vegetable patch. By this time modern extensions had been built onto the old paper mill buildings, and the chimney for the former steam engine had been truncated. This view is now a main road.

Joynson's Paper Mill, St. Mary Cray. Commercial postcard, 1930s.

This aerial photograph was taken when the new bypass to the village was under construction, seen in the foreground. The railway line, crossing the viaduct, is to the right. The paper mill buildings had grown enormously, and here completely fill the constricted site. Later, part became a paper-making museum for a short time, but now the whole complex has totally disappeared.

Upper Paper Mill *(See also p.16)*

A short distance below Snelling's Mill once stood the upper of St. Mary Cray's two paper mills. It used to be southwest of the church, but, in my youth, no trace could be seen. This was perhaps hardly surprising, as production appears to have ceased as early as 1834.[7] The available head of water would have been limited, suggesting the use of a breast wheel. After the demise of the mill the potential was not wasted. By keeping the water at a high level it was possible to augment the head at the larger paper mill a short distance downstream.

Joynson's Paper Mill *(See also p.16)*

The lower paper mill was always known to us as Joynson's Mill, as it had been run by that eminent family for almost a hundred years prior to its closure in about 1928.[8] It was later taken over by Wiggins Teape, but had been demolished completely by the time I revisited the site in 1975. When I knew the mill it was a large complex, predominantly of yellow brick, with a tall, round chimney. The buildings were mostly of the 20th century,

although parts were clearly older, and the river rushed under it with some force.

Immediately upstream of the mill, on the right-hand bank, was the churchyard. This was a very good vantage point from which to study the water arrangements. There were sluices from which a headrace ran into the mill on the opposite bank. A short distance downstream of the sluice was a wide, stepped spillway in yellow brick. It used to form a beautiful cascade with clear water flowing over it, but this, too, is now but a memory. The available head at this mill must have been at least 8 or 9 feet, so that the waterwheel could have been breast-shot or overshot, probably the latter, but it had long-gone. When 16 I was fortunate enough to get to know Mr. Nicholls of Downe, an old man of 94, who could remember the iron waterwheel being visible once, when part of the old mill was being demolished. He was a lad then, and used to visit his uncle, who was the mill foreman. At that time strawberries used to be grown along the river-bank here. Even in 1955 to visualise such a scene needed a certain degree of imagination, but, since then, the whole area immediately west and north-west of the church has changed beyond belief. Not a trace survives of the complex of paper-mill buildings, and where the mill leat used to run is now a busy road!

Nash's Paper Mill, St. Paul's Cray (See also p.19)

The next mill was at St. Paul's Cray, where an ancient traditional corn mill had become a mixed- use site by the 18th century, with three waterwheels. One of these wheels was still grinding corn, but the other two were dressing leather.[9] Papermaking had been established here by 1742,[10] and it developed into a large establishment that was run by the Nash family for over a hundred years. The two illustrations, about a hundred years apart, give an idea of how dramatic had been the changes. Although the complex spanned the river, by 1954 it had the appearance of a modern factory and no evidence of the use of water power was to be seen. To me the place held little appeal and I never ventured inside the gates, although the paper mill complex seemed to have changed subtly every time I cycled past. On a return visit in 1986, I was amazed to find everything had disappeared. Not only had the buildings been demolished,

but the whole watercourse was completely changed. Whereas it used to flow under the road into the mill, it had now been diverted westwards, channelled within high concrete walls.

Foots Cray Mill (See also p.19)

This was another paper mill, a short distance downstream from the bridge where the main road crossed the River Cray. By about 1870 it had become a fabric printing works, changing to the manufacture of photographic film before the turn of the century. Its final use was in silk processing, until eventually the old wooden buildings were demolished in 1929,[11] and a factory was built on the site. Unfortunately I was never able to investigate to see if any evidence of the water-powered era had survived. The large bus garage nearby was, at that time of my life, a target of sufficient interest to tempt me away. The mill site was not easy of access, and from a distance, the modern factory did not appear to my young eyes to have any appeal whatsoever, apart, of course, from the river flowing underneath. In its paper-making days the mill was a fine example, illustrating how much power this chalk-fed stream possessed, only three and a half miles from its source. There were

Nash's Paper Mill, St. Paul's Cray. Drawing, artist unkown, c.1820
This drawing shows the rural character of the valley of the River Cray at this time, and the small scale of what had already become an important paper mill. It is interesting that the demand for power was greater than could be obtained from the river alone, so the steam engine chimney already dominated the scene.

Nash's Paper Mill, St. Paul's Cray. Commercial postcard, c.1920

A contrasting view from a similar position about a century later. Of the buildings and chimney, all had been replaced. A modern factory complex now occupied the site of the old paper mill, and the road had been widened to take the lorries with their heavy loads. Now the whole site has been cleared.

Foots Cray Mill. Commercial postcard, pre-1929

The view looking downstream from the main road bridge. The river is seen flowing freely by this time. Formerly it would have been impounded here, building up the head for the two powerful overshot waterwheels, beneath the building, which once powered the paper-making machinery. By the time this photograph was taken, even the subsequent fabric printing phase for the mill seems to have come to an end. It was completely demolished in about 1929.

Old Mill Bexley. Photographer unknown. Pre-1967

The view from downstream, with the old mill to the right and a much later extension to the left. The River Cray re-appeared from the pair of arches. The wide right-hand arch was the tailrace from the waterwheel and the narrow one was the bypass channel. Seen from the main road, this was a very well-known, and much photographed, scene until May, 1966.

once two overshot waterwheels in parallel here, each 15 feet in diameter. One was 10 feet 6 inches wide and drove four rag-engines, and the other was 5 feet wide and powered two more.[12] The meagre flow in the River Cray these days shows how dramatically this has been reduced since it fed such powerful industrial waterwheels.

North Cray and Vale Mascal

From Foots Cray Mill the River Cray soon flowed through open countryside. Beyond Foots Cray church it ran in the grounds of North Cray Place, a former mansion. The river here was crossed by an attractive bridge, once carrying a drive to the house. Associated with this bridge was a timber weir which dammed back the river, forming a long stretch of deep, relatively still water. I could see no sign of the use of water power here, although it seemed a waste of this natural resource. Further on it was the turn of the Vale Mascal Estate, with further weirs. There, it has been said, there was some evidence suggesting that a waterwheel had once been used for pumping water, but this was a private site I never had the opportunity to visit.

Old Mill, Bexley *(See also p.20)*

Old Mill, Bexley was the only remaining example of a traditional mill building to remain on the River Cray. It was an impressive white weatherboarded structure

Old Mill, Bexley. Alan Stoyel, 10th April 1954

The view from upstream was seldom seen. Here is the truncated chimney of the steam engine. In the mill's working days the water would have been impounded here, controlled by sluices, and forming a relatively deep pool. Unconstrained, the water now runs freely through the former wheel-race and bypass.

Old Mill, Bexley . Alan Stoyel, 4th June 1966

The tragic scene after the fire, showing how completely the old mill building had been destroyed. The shortened chimney is visible in the background. In the foreground the wider of the two tail-race arches can be seen where the water flowed away from the waterwheel.

spanning the stream. I well remember the finely-carved "1779" on one of the internal beams, and this was certainly a likely date for the building. None of the working parts had survived, although there was sufficient evidence to show that there had formerly been an impressive internal low-breast waterwheel, 14 feet in diameter and 10 feet wide, driving four pairs of stones.

When I investigated this mill it was being used by a sack-making firm. I was accompanied by a patient worker who was as helpful as he could be. At 14, however, I was untutored in the art of sifting reliable information from the speculative. A little knowledge is a dangerous thing! When I was told that the millstones had been "blue and about six feet across", I thought these must have been the bluish grey "Cullin" stones from Germany. I had read about them but had never seen one, and. I knew they were once popular in various parts of England. It was some years later, after my father and I had published a joint article on the mill,[13] that Peter Davies took me to task, rightly pointing out the impossibility of both size and stone type that I had recorded so niaively. It was a lesson I would never forget.

There was a truncated square brick chimney-stack on the upstream side of the mill, away from the road. This was all that remained of the auxiliary steam engine which had been added in about 1884. Apparently the steeplejack responsible for this chimney, a Mr. Hart from Lancashire, had the misfortune to fall from the top of it, when doing some repairs soon afterwards. Seriously injured, he lived to tell the tale, his fall having been broken by the slate roof of the engine house.[14]

From about 1840 onwards Old Mill was operated by the Cannon family, and it is said that it was due to the success of Stephen Cannon's business here that the firm of Cannon & Gaze Ltd. embarked on the huge expansion of the Erith Flour Mills in 1891.[15] These were massive steam-powered roller mills using imported grain, straight off the ships. Despite the fact that the water at the dock was not as deep as was found necessary, the cycle of milling development in NW Kent had been completed. It was the death-knell for the local water-powered flour mills, which could no longer compete.

It was a great shock when I learned of the total destruction of Bexley Mill by fire on 12th May 1966.[16] On a visit to Kent three weeks later I viewed the sad remains. The scorched brick base and a few tortured steel girders were all that survived of the mill itself. Within a fairly short time a new "Old" Mill had risen from the ashes as a public house, desperately mimicking what had gone before. It is likely that many people now are una-

ware that the present building is not the one which had graced this spot for nearly two hundred years. To anyone with an affinity for old buildings, however, it is all too obvious. With the disappearance of this impressive mill a significant chapter in the history of the River Cray had ended.

Hall Place Mill, Bexley

(See also p.23 & 24)

Behind Hall Place, a lovely 16th and 17th century house, once stood an impressive weatherboarded mill. I first visited the open site where once it had stood on a cold January day in 1953, and found modern sluices allowing the water to rush through the two bypass channels, although part of the flow was still passing through the brick wheel-race alongside, to the right. There had once been a powerful low-breast waterwheel, approximately fourteen feet in diameter and nine feet six inches wide, as shown by the curvature of the breast-work and the curved marking on the side-wall. In the garden of the house I found four millstones, each of four feet diameter; two French burrs and two Peak stones, but, of the mill itself, nothing could be seen.

Traditionally it had been a corn mill, and old pictures show it to have been a much larger and more impressive structure than might have been imagined. Here, too, the Cannon family were millers for a time. The last direc-

Opposite Top: Hall Place Mill, Bexley. Alan Stoyel, 4th July 1954

Fifty years ago the site where the waterwheel had once been was clearly to be seen. Its former diameter and width could still be measured, and the river still flowed over the breast-work which had once kept the water in contact with the wheel. Much of this evidence has since been obliterated. For most of the time the present flow in the river would be insufficient to have powered such a large wheel.

Opposite Bottom: Hall Place Mill, Bexley. Commercial postcard, c.1905

When this photograph was taken the mill does not have the look of a working building, although its general appearance is good. The fenestration has clearly been changed, and it looks as if a few alterations are still in the process of being carried out. It is difficult to reconcile this image of such a large mill building with what is now such an unprepossessing site.

Hall Place Mill, Bexley. E.C. Youens, c.1890s

This is another view of the mill, taken from a very impressive angle, demonstrating the size of the building. The lucomb projects further from the front of the mill than is normally the case. Although all the boarding and windows look to be in good condition, the building does not have a well-used appearance.

tory entry for a corn miller here appears to have been in 1882. A new lease of life for it was found as a silk printing and flag-making works, an extension of the long-established industry at Crayford, further downstream. This use seems to have continued until shortly before the First World War, after which the mill's condition deteriorated. Talking to old local inhabitants, one, Mr. Frank Buckland, had actually witnessed the old weather-boarded mill being pulled down with a traction engine in about 1925. Apparently some of the main beams from the mill were then shipped to America for a Mr. Brady, a millionaire, to be used in a mansion there.[17]

Evans's Printing Works and Galbraith's Printing Works, Crayford

On the left bank of the river, as it enters Crayford, was a sprawling complex of low buildings which comprised

the silk printing works of David Evans. The industry began in Crayford in the late 17th century and spread gradually, but this historic works was the first to be established here and the last to survive. Previously owned by Augustus Applegarth, it was bought by David Evans in the 1840s. I suspected there had probably been a waterwheel here originally, and I was keen to see if anything remained. When I called at this fascinating place, I was made welcome, and was shown the process of printing using traditional hand blocks. I still have a block from this works, which I treasure. When I asked about the historical use of a waterwheel here, I was told, in no uncertain manner, that the river Cray had supplied process water only, and that it had never been used as a source of power. This was one of the first times I remained unconvinced by my informant. Similar premises to this on the Cray, Darent and other rivers, had capitalised on what water power was available, if only for pumping process water or for washing the fabrics, and this

Swaisland's Printing Works, Crayford. Alan Stoyel, 25th January 1961

The mill building on the East bank of the river, viewed from downstream. In the foreground is the tail-race arch, and the low weir in the background is where the water was diverted into the building to drive the waterwheel. There was probably a similar arrangement at one time to the right of the picture, where it is thought there was once a second waterwheel.

Crayford Flour Mill, Crayford. Alan Stoyel, 25th January 1961.

Although it is clearly of at least two generations, the whole of the main mill building is completely modern. The base of the old chimney for the steam engine was still in place, and the gap between it and the main mill building was where the waterwheel had once been. Although the mill pond has shrunk, its shape suggests there may once have been a second waterwheel to the right of the picture, probably to drive the sawmill. The view has changed considerably since this picture was taken.

establishment was of such old foundation. Unfortunately I never had the chance of investigating the evidence for myself. With subsequent redevelopment of the site the opportunity has now gone for ever.

The next water-powered site appears to have been where Galbraith's silk printing works once stood, just upstream of the bridging point of Watling Street. Early mills were frequently established just upstream of river crossings, and, since this had been an important highway since Roman times, the mill site is probably an ancient one. There was also a tannery in this area at one time, I believe, but unfortunately all had disappeared before I was able to investigate this stretch of the river.

Swaisland's Printing Works, Crayford (See also p.25)

This was once the largest of the Crayford fabric printing works and, at its height, it employed five hundred people.[18] The only part that showed any evidence of having been water-powered was an unprepossessing, single-storeyed, late 19th century brick building on the right-hand bank. Near the upstream end of the building was a low weir with sluices, and, a short distance downstream, a brick arch showed where the tailrace rejoined the river.

Founded by Charles Swaisland in 1812, the works had been in the hands of G.P. & J. Baker Ltd. since 1893.[19] I called there with my father one day in 1954. We were made welcome and were told that the Swaisland records go back 280 years. We were taken to where the internal waterwheel had been formerly, and its use was explained. The wheel had been a low-breast one of iron and wood construction, only about 10 feet diameter by 6 feet wide, driving two large wooden drums for fabric washing by means of overhead shafting. Apparently the firm operating the flour mills downstream controlled the water rights, so this wheel's use could only be intermittent. The waterwheel had eventually been removed in 1947-8.

One informant told me that there had once been a second waterwheel at the works, and that it survived into the period of Baker's ownership. Certainly there are two waterwheel symbols shown at this spot on Greenwood's map of 1821[20]. In all probability the other wheel would have been located in a similar building on the left-hand bank of the river, fed from the same weir.

Fifty years later I returned to see how the building had fared, but the whole area had been redeveloped to such an extent that I could not even be sure of where it had stood. All landmarks and reference features seem to have been swept away, and the river was now confined ignominiously within walls of ugly grey concrete.

Barnes Cray Printing Works, Crayford

There was once another mill for printing fabrics somewhere near where Maiden Lane intersects the River Cray at Barnes Cray. Nothing remains of it, nor am I certain that it ever had a waterwheel. It was marked on Greenwood's map[21] as "Calico Printing Mills", and I spoke to elderly local inhabitants who could vaguely remember its existence, but knew nothing of the means by which it was powered. If it did once have a waterwheel it is likely that the available head was utilised by the flour mills further downstream, as they controlled the water rights and were always hungry for more power. The river here is solidly embanked, and at a relatively high level. There is no trace of where any waterwheel might have been located. If there ever was one here, it must have disappeared a very long time ago.

Crayford Flour Mill (See also p.25)

This was the lowest mill site on the River Cray, and its history was complicated. By 1570 water-powered machinery was making iron plates for armour here.[22] In about 1817 iron working was superseded by a corn mill on the left bank, for a time sharing the available water with a sawmill, which had developed alongside.

By the time I visited the place in April 1954 there was little historic fabric remaining, and extensive building work being carried out on the flour mills at the time prevented a proper site investigation. By then it was a modern, electrically driven roller-mill, known as the "Vitbe" Flour Mills. This proprietary name had been coined in 1927 to promote a flour which retained more of the beneficial vitamin B.[23] There was little to be seen which would have been older than 20th century in date. The building was tall, stark, four storeys high, and it appeared to be in the process of being superseded by an even taller one of five storeys. The mill was situated on the left bank at the end of what had been a fair-sized pond. Running south-eastwards from the building, was a long, low brick range with a corrugated iron roof. At the mill end of this range was a large, truncated square brick chimney on a plinth. Its position, separated from the mill only by the former wheel-race, suggested it to have been for a steam engine supplying auxiliary power for the corn-grinding machinery.

I talked to a middle-aged man on site who had worked at the mill all his life. He had known it since about 1914 and, because of his familiarity with milling, he was able to give my young ears some tantalising fragments of information. Apparently there used to be an inscribed stone on the building, and he thought it bore the date of 1817.[24] He also said there had been five pairs of 4ft.6ins. French burr millstones driven by fairly conventional machinery.[25] The power came from a large iron breast-shot waterwheel which was outside the main building, but roofed-over. This wheel was reputed to measure 28ft. in diameter by 8ft. 6ins. wide, with the water entry only a foot below shaft level. Of this diameter of waterwheel, however, I have always been sceptical, although I admit that everything else my informant told me had a real ring of authenticity to it.

He said most of the old machinery had been removed in about 1909, from which time all the milling was car-ried out with roller plant driven by gas engines, the waterwheel being used for hoisting only. The wooden upright shaft, still with half of the cast-iron wallower attached to it, was eventually pulled out of the building in 1914, and it was then, too, that the waterwheel was scrapped. The river was tidal up to this point, and much of the wheat and flour used to be conveyed to and from the mill by boat.[26]

Over fifty years later I returned to find most of the mill building had gone, leaving only the part which I had seen being erected on my first visit, huge, derelict and dangerous. Gone, too, was the old range with the chimney base. Once again an investigation of where the waterwheel had been was impossible because of safety restrictions, and the last remaining building on this historic site was due to disappear very shortly. I could only view it from a safe distance, but I could see the opening in the dock wall below the mill where the tail-water from the wheel would once have entered the tidal basin.

The River Darent

The stream rises in the Lower Greensand and flows northwards to Westerham, where it turns, following the Gault Clay outcrop eastwards towards Sevenoaks. This part of the valley is dominated by the chalk downs on the northern side. Just north of Sevenoaks some tributaries come in from the south, and from the eastward continuation of the Gault Clay vale. Here the Darent turns northwards and has cut straight through the chalk of the North Downs producing an attractive, steep sided valley. As the river flows further into the London basin its lower course duplicates that of the Cray, crossing much younger sands and gravels until it becomes tidal, just north of Dartford, and finally reaches the River Thames.

The Darent is considerably longer than the Cray, and, because it rises so much further from the London sprawl, it has retained more of its rural character. The whole course of the river has remained in Kent. Nevertheless, the disappearance of its mills, coupled with the effects of water abstraction, have been dramatic. The length of the main stream is approximately 21 miles. In its prime it and its tributaries have driven over 40 waterwheels.

There are 37 locations on the Darent where water power appears to have been used. Some have been multiple complexes, the most notable being the Dartford Powder Mills, which is here considered as a single site. Many of these mills have seen changes of function, so the following analysis is an over-simplification. In particular, I have omitted Phoenix Mills because of their complicated history of different uses. 22 mills were primarily for grinding corn, of which 9 had disappeared before I started my investigation, 7 have either gone, or been savagely altered since I first saw them, and 6 remain virtually unchanged. However, none of these now contains its working parts. Of the paper mill complexes, 4 of the 7 have been demolished since I first knew them, and not a single one remains standing today.

Other water-powered sites were for silk processing, fabric printing, sawing, gunpowder production, electricity generation and water pumping. Out of all these functions just one water-wheel powered installation in the whole of the Darent valley, a water pump, had managed to survive when I saw it in 1980.

Spring Shaw Mill or Squerryes Park Mill, Westerham
(See also p.29 & 30)

I discovered this site when I was 15, and assumed that here used to be a water-powered pump-house supplying water to the Squerryes Estate. Along the track a few hundred yards before reaching the mill site was the ominous thumping of a hydraulic ram. With each loud thump you could feel the vibration in the ground itself; it was menacing and eerie. This was the first hydraulic ram that I had come across. It seemed logical to me that this would have superseded the waterwheel-driven pump. However, I found I had been wrong in my conjecture, as the mill appears to have been for grinding corn. It was shown as such on the 6 inches to the mile Ordnance Survey map, although it had already become disused by the time of the 1890s revision.

All that remained of the mill by the Spring of 1955 were some wall-bases and piles of rubble. The building had been very small, approximately 17 feet square externally, of rubble stone with brick details, and a tiled roof. It was built into the bank of an attractive tree-fringed pond, about 120 yards long. There had been two storeys, the upper one opening onto the top of the dam. On the east side there had once been an external, overshot waterwheel of the order of 9 or 10 feet in diameter by about 3 feet wide, but all that remained of the working parts was a circular wooden shaft, about 11½ inches in diameter, of which about 9 feet 6 inches was visible, sticking out of the rubble. At one point were two open mortises for the four compass arms of a wooden gear and, about 8 feet further along the shaft, was a single rectangular mortise through it. This could once have been the upright shaft of a small corn mill, although there was no definitive evidence. Some years later I called back to see if any more of the shaft was visible, but nothing of it had survived, and the whole site had become overgrown.

Elm View Mill, Westerham
(See also p.32-34)

Near the gates to Squerryes Park in the 1950s used to stand an imposing 18th century brick building, without roof or floors. The brickwork was a particularly bright red, and the architecture was distinctive. The main door

Spring Shaw Mill, Westerham. Commercial postcard, c.1900.

This view shows how small the mill was, and how impractical it would have been to operate. The approach could only have been by a path across the dam from the left, and the door in the picture was the one on the upper of the two floors. The waterwheel was on the right-hand side of the mill, below pond level. It is doubtful if the building was still functioning as a mill at this time, although it appears to be in good condition.

Above: Spring Shaw Mill, Westerham. Derek Stoyel, 5th April.1955.

The mill-pond, looking downstream. At the far end of the pond can be seen the dam, upon which once stood the tiny mill. By this time only wall bases and rubble survived of the building.

Left: Spring Shaw Mill, Westerham. Alan Stoyel, 5th April 1955.

An old wooden shaft lying in the remains of the mill. This was only partly visible, but may have been the upright shaft in the mill. At the end of the shaft can be seen the iron pintle, which once ran in a bearing. Near the end is an open mortise. This mortise intersected a similar one at 90 degrees to it, and these would formerly have embraced the two pieces of wood which made up the four compass-arms of a wooden gear.

and loading door had semi-circular heads, and the windows were circular. An external iron overshot waterwheel was still in place. The wheel measured exactly 12 feet in diameter by 33½ inches wide and, unusually, it had iron spur gears beyond the outer bearing, with a crank and sweep-rod on the downstream side. Inside the mill all that remained was a massive cast-iron pitwheel which had lost most of its wooden cogs. This was the first waterwheel I ever measured. The whole place had a sense of magic, with clear water disappearing underground, re-appearing mysteriously some way away, beneath the bole of a huge tree.

What brought an extra dimension of excitement to this mill was the meeting there of a very old man who was then 99, Mr. Nicholas, who had known the mill all his life. He told me he remembered the waterwheel being installed, replacing an old wooden one. For someone who was coming close to his 14th birthday to learn that this exciting event had occurred in 1868 when he, Mr. Nicholas, was 14, was a surreal experience which was immediately etched indelibly in my memory. I treasured my time with this delightful old man. I realised what invaluable conversations could be had with such people if they were prompted with probing questions. What he did was to bring this derelict shell of a mill back to life, helping me to visualise it in its working state, so long before. About a year later I learnt that Mr. Nicholas was ill and, soon after, that he had died. He had passed on information freely to me that may never have been given to anybody else – probably simply because they had not been sufficiently interested, or had not asked the right questions. I was lucky enough to be the recipient of fascinating facts of which perhaps nobody else still living was aware! I was now totally hooked. From now on every watermill was something to be investigated, and every elderly person was somebody to be interviewed.

Mr. Nicholas showed me where the wooden penstock used to be, which controlled the water to the wheel. He pointed to where a shed had once stood by the mill, where the miller used to keep a pony and trap. He enabled me to visualise the miller himself, leaning over the stable door, above a couple of steps, at the front of his mill.

About 1890 the waterwheel had been adapted to pump water for the town of Westerham at an average supply of 25,000 gallons a day from a nearby well in the lower greensand. This was the only waterwheel to provide water for the Metropolitan Water Board and it last turned for pumping on May 12th 1907.[27] The milling machinery was removed in about 1936. The mill was already in bad condition before the Second World War, and then a flying

bomb in a nearby field blew much of the roof off. It was never repaired.

Eventually, in July 1960, I arrived one day to find the whole building gone. The upper part of the pitwheel and the outstretched, pleading arms of the smashed waterwheel projected from a mass of shattered brickwork. An act of vandalism had occurred which I found difficult to accept, let alone to understand. Westerham had lost one of its most attractive and historic landmarks.

Darenth Mill, Westerham
(See also p.35)

From Elm View Mill the Darent runs round the south side of the town. Just west of the road leading southwards to Crockham Hill used to stand Darenth Mill. I never understood why the "h" had been tacked onto the stream's name to become the name of this mill. Was there some connection with the village, of that name and spelling, which stands much lower down the River Darent's course? Or was it just a spelling mistake which stuck?

Its location, tucked in close to the town centre, suggests it was probably the first of Westerham's mills, and it was certainly the last of them to grind corn. Largely weatherboarded, with an external overshot waterwheel, it had finally stopped by about the outbreak of the First World War. In the 1930s it was demolished and its place was later taken by a shed, leaving little evidence that a mill had ever existed here. Exactly where the mill had stood was pointed out to me by an elderly gentleman, who said the wheel had driven two pairs of millstones. I was grateful for this information, but the site was a disappointment to me. So much had gone, virtually without trace, within about 30 years. This was one of my early mill excursions and, for the first time, there were no physical remains which could be recorded; nothing to measure, describe or photograph.

Valence Water Pump, Brasted

When I was living in Kent I was unaware of this interesting relic. Having heard rumours of its existence, I did not actually see it until 1980, nineteen years after I had left the county, but it was worth the wait. An iron high-breast waterwheel and associated pumping machinery still survived on an overgrown and fairly remote site on the Brasted-Westerham parish boundary. The 16 feet diameter waterwheel was 3 feet 5 inches wide between the shrouds, and was completely of iron. No inscrip-

Elm View Mill, Westerham. Aquatint by G. Samuel, published in 1812.

An illustration of Elm View Mill, Westerham in its working days. The stable building seen to the left disappeared long ago, although I remember the scar still being visible on the corner of the mill where it had once been. The waterwheel is shown here with the water passing beneath it. Is this merely artist's licence? Or was the head increased at a later date to enable an overshot waterwheel to be installed, thus producing considerably more power?

Elm View Mill, Westerham. Unknown photographer, April 1954.

An excellent photograph demonstrating the symmetry and elegance of this late eighteenth century mill. Its character was unique and its loss was tragic. It is interesting to note the scar of the former stable building, still visible on the left-hand corner of the mill – evidence of the accuracy of the 1812 illustration. The iron overshot waterwheel of 1868 is to the right of the mill.

Elm View Mill, Westerham. Alan Stoyel, 5th September 1954

The overshot iron waterwheel at Elm View Mill showing the extra gears for driving the water pump. The bent iron rod running across the waterwheel was for controlling the water flow to the wheel, and was operated by a lever inside the mill.

Elm View Mill, Westerham. Alan Stoyel, 9th. July 1960

This is a similar view to the one above, taken 6 years later. It shows the chaos resulting from demolition of the mill, before the site was cleared. The pitwheel, formerly inside the mill, is now exposed to view - on the left-hand side.

tion could be seen on it, although the date of 1858 had been cut into a stone built into the wheel-pit. This was quite a likely date for the installation. A 6 feet diameter iron spur-geared pitwheel drove a pinion, mounted on a crankshaft, on each side. From each crankshaft ran a sweep rod to a vertical ram pump of 14inches stroke and 5½ inches bore. This wheel pumped water for the Valence Estate, but had been out of use for a considerable time. As far as I was aware this was the only traditional waterwheel remaining in the whole Darent valley; a precious survival.

Mill Farm, Brasted *(See also p.37)*

I did not know of this mill until one fine May day in 1954 when, admiring a very handsome detached brick house with a Sun firemark, I noticed an inscription on the building which said "this Mill House was built in the yeare 1705". I looked at the cluster of attractive buildings at the rear, one of which was built into a high bank and could well have once been a mill. It was a relatively insignificant structure with brick side-walls, a weatherboarded gable-end and a tiled roof. Formerly driven by a tributary stream, milling had obviously ceased a long time ago. Directory entries show that this was indeed a corn mill, apparently operated by three generations of the Smith family, the last entry seen being in 1878. This tied in with information from an elderly local inhabitant, who told me that the iron waterwheel and all the machinery had been removed some time prior to the

Darenth Mill, Westerham. Commercial postcard, probably c.1910.

The good state of the weatherboarding and the waterwheel is indicative that the mill was still in regular work at the time this photograph was taken. The overshot wheel has a square shaft, two sets of eight arms and buckets which are all of iron. The shrouds appear to be of wood, with an iron strap nailed around the periphery to keep the arrangement tight. Such a construction would deteriorate rapidly once regular used ceased. The long rod running along the mill wall above the wheel is for raising or lowering the penstock, controlling the water onto the wheel, the adjustment carried out from the meal floor (the lowest storey) inside the mill. The steeply-inclined wooden ducting running down the mill wall is probably ducting from a grain cleaner, all the extracted dust and rubbish being blown down it into the tailrace.

First World War.

At the time of my visit an adjacent building was in use as a dairy, but the mill now served purely as a garage, with large double doors inserted in the weatherboarded gable end. The stream had been diverted from the once stone- and brick-edged millpond, which now supported a flourishing orchard, perched on an impressive earth bank. The mill itself was built into this bank, with a door opening from the tile-hung loft gable onto the edge of the pond. The position of the former external waterwheel was clear, although where its shaft entered the building was apparently below the level to which the wheel-pit had been in-filled. The brick wall at the upstream end of the pit was still there, coated with layers of tufa from many years of exposure to the lime-laden water trickling down it. The wheel appeared to have been overshot, of estimated size at least 14 feet diameter by perhaps 3 feet wide.

Inside the building, near the north-west corner, the bricked-up hole through which the wheel-shaft once passed could still be made out. This and a small pulley, suspended from the very centre of the ridge of the roof, through which the sack-hoist chain once ran, were now the only signs left of the workings of the mill. There were two storeys and a loft, and it was the loft which fascinated me. There was a central walkway, which had formerly given access to the corn bins on each side. The roof above was plastered, and, drawn on this, were the ghostly shapes of men and horses, apparently traced out with a burning candle. I could only speculate as to when this could have been done, perhaps by some bored young mill-hand, awaiting the arrival of a sack of grain on the hoist, before unhitching it and tipping it into one of the bins.

Brasted Mill *(See also p.39 & 41)*

Brasted Mill is in stark contrast to the mill at Mill Farm, less than half a mile away. It is a more modern and industrial style of building, of three storeys, standing prominently in the relatively flat land bordering the main river Darent. The front, or south, elevation of the mill is formal and fiercely symmetrical, with the upper part of the central gable projected forward by several feet. This unique structure is like a broad lucomb, extending the full width of the gable, supported on substantial timbers, and giving protection to the three central doors, one above the other. Apart from the ground floor, of brick and Kentish rag-stone, the remainder of this front is weatherboarded. It carries a prominent date of "1881" picked out in

wrought iron-work attached to an upper panel in the first-floor loading door. Field evidence suggested this was a southern extension to an earlier nineteenth century brick building which had also been extended eastwards to complete the symmetry of the T-shaped plan.

When I visited the mill in 1954 it appeared to be in use as a house. The mill-pond had been filled and levelled and all the working parts removed. The owner was most welcoming and he took me round the side of the building to where the waterwheel had once turned. It had been a breast wheel, the furthest upstream of the many breast wheels on the River Darent. The blocked shaft-hole was prominent, a circle framed in red brick on a rag-stone wall, its large size suggesting that a wooden wheelshaft had been installed here as late as 1881. The wheel had been about 12-13 feet in diameter by about 6 feet 6 inches wide.

Because I had shown so much interest, my host went to fetch something he thought would interest me. He returned with an old, cracked glass negative showing the front of the mill in its working days, with the mill-pond and waterwheel on the left. He pointed out a chicken coop in the right-hand foreground of the photograph and related how, when that coop was eventually demolished, this very negative was found inside it! When he then actually made me a gift of the surreal object I could hardly believe my good fortune, and it has been a treasured possession ever since. Turning homewards, the pedals on my bicycle had never gone so fast!

From talking to several elderly local residents I learned the mill ceased grinding corn in the 1920s, and, after a brief period running a refrigeration plant, the working parts were removed in about 1934. When I next saw the mill, in 1979, it was part of Locomotors Ltd., Motor Engineers & Coachbuilders, but the building appeared little changed

Sundridge Paper Mill
(See also p.41-43)

When first seen, in May 1954, the range of buildings on this site was of red brick, and of no great age. It extended northwards, away from the main road, and was occupied by West Kent Laundry Ltd. As if a reminder of its current use was necessary, a gentle puff of steam was usually to be seen exuding from the buildings. Immediately against the road, however, was an earlier mill-house of red brick, L-shaped in plan, probably dating from the late 18th century. For a couple of hundred yards upstream of this house ran an elongated mill-pond, an extension

Mill Farm Mill, Brasted. Alan Stoyel, 27th May 1954

The tile-hung mill gable was level with the bank of the pond. The pond has been drained to form an orchard, but the rubble stone-work of the retaining is visible. In the background is the early 18th century mill house.

Mill Farm Mill, Brasted. Derek Stoyel, 21st February 1959

The mill, viewed from the gateway into the yard, showing the inserted garage doors. The mill house is to the right of this picture. The outbuildings were in use as a dairy and bottling plant – hence the stack of crates of milk-bottles beside the mill.

of a leat which formerly ran along the roadside. The water had been diverted and the pond was drained and full of weeds, with an abandoned bypass sluice half-way along its bank. The pond ended in front of the laundry and house, its banks channelled into an iron trough between the two buildings. Clearly this was where the waterwheel had once been; the iron trash-grid, which had stopped debris getting to the wheel, was still in position.

Examination suggested the wheel was overshot, of an estimated size of 12 feet 6 inches diameter by about 6 feet 3 inches wide, and some scratch-marks on the brickwork of the pit were visible. Nearby was a truncated brick chimney-stack. I engaged various elderly local residents in conversation and I gathered that the wheel was, indeed, overshot, and that the shaft was a wooden one until the end. One old man could remember the wheel-shaft being replaced by a massive square one of oak from Lord Stanhope's estate at Chevening. The mill used to make high quality paper for Bank of England notes, but the business was transferred to Eynsford Paper Mill, and Sundridge Mill closed in about 1901. Prior to this about fifty people had been employed. Almost immediately after paper production ceased, the buildings were bought by the laundry, and they were rebuilt and extended in 1913-14. It was then that the waterwheel was removed, replaced by steam power. Apparently the wheelshaft was still sound enough at that time to be sawn up and used for making coffins!

Mr. Brealey, who lived nearby, was kind enough to give me various historical references to the mill, and it was clear that it was of ancient foundation. Almost certainly, it occupied one of three Domesday sites at Sundridge. It would appear the change from corn milling to paper manufacture occurred in the mid 18th century, and that this use continued uninterrupted until the beginning of the 20th.

One kind old man gave me a rather battered old postcard showing the mill from upstream at some time before 1914. It really opened my eyes to the changes which had occurred during the lifetimes of my informants. It shows how impressive the mill-pond was, and how different from the brick laundry the earlier paper-mill building had been. Here was formerly a long range, more or less on the same footprint, but an altogether more impressive structure, the upper part fitted with vertical wooden louvres for drying the paper. Two other details on the postcard were of particular interest. The brick mill-house building was shown as extending a further twelve feet or so from the road, where it butted against the end of the drying-loft range. Within this extra length of brickwork could be clearly seen an arch, a headrace arch. So the waterwheel had been an internal one – something I had not suspected. The other detail was a chimney stack, quite close to where the waterwheel would have been, showing that steam power had not been introduced by the laundry to supersede the waterwheel, as had been implied by my informants. Clearly a steam engine had been used to assist the waterwheel at a much earlier date, while the paper mill was still in operation.

When I returned to see the site in October 1969 I found the laundry buildings in the late stages of demolition, but the mill-house was still standing. A further visit in September 1975 found the old mill-house to have been pulled down some time before, although the waterwheel-pit was still recognisable. Finally, in June 1979, I saw that this ancient site had been totally obliterated, landscaped to form a characterless grassy bank.

Chipstead Mill, Chevening
(See also p.43 & 45)

This was a flour mill which had lost its waterwheel and machinery only about eight years before I visited it in May 1954. It was a large, and very unattractive, building on the left bank of the river, although a delightful 18th century mill-house, L-shaped in plan, stood on the right bank. The two were separated by a cascade, of the order of 6 feet high, showing where the former waterwheel had been. Nothing remained inside the building, I was told by the man who was living in the house. The mill was locked, having just been sold to a Bromley grocer for storage, so I was unable to see if any internal evidence remained. The depth and volume of water between the two buildings prevented any investigation of the waterwheel area, although the blocked opening where the wheelshaft had entered the building was clearly visible. The original large circular shaft-hole had been reduced in size, before being totally in-filled, suggesting that the wheel-shaft had originally been wooden, later replaced by a smaller one of iron. The shaft position was below the sill of the waterfall, and the back of the wheelpit was vertical, so the wheel was presumed to have been overshot.

The existing four-storeyed mill building was of uncompromising modern red brick. Considerable ragstone fabric occupying much of the bottom two storeys showed that an earlier mid 19th-century stone structure had been more than doubled in height. This looked as if it had occurred at about the end of the 19th century, and probably coincided with a change from stone-ground

Brasted Mill. The front of the mill; Derek Stoyel, 21st February 1959

The mill has long been gutted of its waterwheel and machinery, but is still in good condition. The upper loading-door has been replaced by a window, the window in the strangely-extended lucomb has gone, a domestic chimney has been added, the main doorway has been widened, and extra widows inserted to the left, but the building has managed to retain its character. The mill pond had been in-filled by this time.

Brasted Mill. The mill from the South; unknown photographer, c.1920.

The mill was still at work, and the mill-pond and water-wheel can be seen to the left. When the hen coop in the right foreground was de-molished, the glass negative from which this picture was print-ed was found inside it – hence the break!

flour to roller milling. Subsequently further extensions were added. In earlier times it is probable that the house formed part of a single range which incorporated the mill, and the waterwheel would therefore once have been internal. The only mechanical items to be seen were two abandoned millstones nearby. These were French burr-stones, 48 inches in diameter, one of them having an iron maker's plate of Hughes and Sons of London.

My informant from the house confirmed the wheel to have been overshot, and said that it, and the rest of the machinery, was mostly of iron, all removed for scrap by a firm from Tunbridge Wells between about 1946 and 1950. He thought two pairs of French burrs had been driven by the wheel, but there may also have been a third pair of stones. A steam engine had provided auxiliary power, he added, followed by a 75 horse-power suction gas engine, but finally everything was driven by electricity. Roller mills were installed here around the 1890s, he concluded, but milling came to an end in about the late 1920s.

I saw the mill again in October 1964, but little had changed. There were various reports in the 1980s of plans to demolish the mill and redevelop the site, but I have not been back.

Longford Mill, Dunton Green

(See also p.47 & 48)

This was the first Kentish mill of which I have a memory, but the building has now disappeared completely. Always a particular favourite of mine, I have witnessed various stages in its demise. Longford Mill used to stand on the West side of the main road between Dunton Green and Riverhead, and yet it was just within the large parish of Otford until Dunton Green became a separate point. Despite the relatively low gradient of the valley by this point, the waterwheel was overshot – the furthest down-stream for an overshot wheel on the main River Darent, as far as I am aware. The first time I saw it was in March 1948, on a local cycle ride with my father. The wide internal waterwheel was clearly visible, but not turning. He and I sat on a wall, just downstream, and we each sketched the mill. The two results could hardly have been more different!

By the time of my next visit, in May 1953, the mill yard had been extended over the tail-race, filling it in and covering it with tarmac. The infill was pushed up against the iron wheel, leaving only a small air-gap at the top of the tailrace arch for the wheel to breathe. The ground floor wall of the mill had always been of brick,

the remainder weatherboarded. Very recently, however, the brickwork had been extended upwards, leaving only a narrow strip of boarding beneath the eaves, and the attractive first floor sashes had been replaced by unsympathetic, modern, wide windows beneath long concrete lintels. Bitterly disappointed, I was consoled by the thought that at least the waterwheel was safe – and out of the reach of scrap-men.

I had never seen an overshot waterwheel of these proportions. Its diameter was only about 7 feet, although it was approximately 12 feet wide. The wheel was completely of iron, constructed in four bays, with five sets of arms, on an iron shaft and fed by an iron pentrough. For such a small diameter overshot waterwheel to have been installed was presumably to capitalise on the available head, giving an increased rotational speed. It would probably have replaced a much larger breast wheel, a trend seen in other Kent mills.

On the mill was a stone inscribed "T.C. 1859". Presumably this stood for Thomas Cooke, who was the mill-

Opposite top: Brasted Mill. The site of the former waterwheel; Alan Stoyel, 5th September 1954

In front of this unconventional ragstone rubble wall with red brick detail, the waterwheel once turned. The blocked circular shaft-hole of the wheel is now at ground level. The low wall in the foreground is part of the bypass channel, the water once flowing from right to left. The unusual brick detail above the shaft-hole probably marks where there was a recess on the inside wall to accommodate the spurwheel in the drive to the millstones. Because of the reduced thickness of wall at this point, bricks were substituted for the ragstone, and a relieving arch was introduced over the top.

Opposite bottom: Paper Mill, Sundridge. Buildings from upstream. Alan Stoyel, 14th September 1964

Looking down the line of the overgrown millpond to where the paper mill once stood. The laundry building which replaced it is to the left, and the old mill house to the right, with the steam engine chimney in between. This makes an interesting comparison with the next view, which was taken over 60 years earlier.

Paper Mill, Sundridge. Mill from upstream. Commercial postcard, c.1900

A similar view to the last one, showing the old paper mill building with its wooden-louvred drying lofts. The steam engine chimney is visible and, below it, can be seen the outline of the head-race arch through which the water passed to the overshot waterwheel.

Paper Mill, Sundridge. A close-up from upstream. Alan Stoyel, 27th May 1954

Once again, this makes an interesting comparison with the previous pictures. The gap between the buildings is where the overshot waterwheel used to be, and the iron trash grid, filtering out any rubbish, is still in position at the end of the dry millpond. This trash grid marks the position of the headrace arch, seen in the last illustration, the end two bays of the mill house having been demolished.

Paper Mill, Sundridge. Demolition of the house; Alan Stoyel, 23rd October 1969.

The remainder of the old mill house has just come down, exposing some very old walling and timber framing of the paper mill, together with the attractive steam engine chimney. All the buildings soon fell prey to the bulldozer, and the whole site was completely cleared.

Chipstead Mill, Chevening. House from the Southeast. Alan Stoyel, 3rd October 1964

The rear of the mill house showing its decorative brick-work and elegant hipped roof. The mill is to the left, and the gap between the two buildings is where the waterwheel used to be. Some rag-stone walling is visible in the lower part of the rebuilt brick mill.

er here in 1858,[28] and the date appeared reasonable for this latest rebuilding. The adjoining mill-house to the Southeast carried a similar stone with "LONGFORD 1859" on it. The mill and house formed one continuous range with the wheel in the centre, the first and second floors of the house extending over the waterwheel. It was said that when the mill was working hard the pictures used to rattle in these rooms. The gable end of the mill bore the scar where there had once been a wooden lucomb. This would have enabled sacks of corn to be hoisted directly onto the walkway, which ran the length of the mill loft, with bins on each side.

It was not until April 1956 that I gained entry to the mill, and I was excited to find, fixed to the hurst frame, a maker's plate "W. WEEKS MILLWRIGHT MAIDSTONE 1859". Clearly the whole site had been redeveloped, structurally and mechanically, in a single phase. Most unfortunately the iron machinery had been taken for scrap, by a firm from Wrotham, only two years before my visit. The positions of the upright shaft, wallower and spurwheel, spindles and stone nuts were plain to see, and there were still three 42-inch Peak bedstones in place on the first floor, but all the rest of the gear had gone. The pathetic half of the smashed-off wooden-cogged, cast-iron pitwheel was still attached, giving the vacated space an atmosphere of squalor.

At this time the mill was still at work, powered by electricity, grinding with more modern machinery, rolling oats and mixing feeds, largely for pigs. The water rights had been sold to the gravel pits operating upstream of the mill, and the water supply had been diverted. In the headrace of the mill could be seen a flourishing vegetable garden, and, beyond it, a dry concrete swimming pool. I was told that lack of water had been an increasing problem, and since 1949-50 the wheel had not worked.

Latterly milling could only be done with a single pair of stones, although the previous old miller was reputed to have had all three pairs running at a time.

When I visited the mill in September 1975 I found the mill-house had been demolished, together with the waterwheel, the mill now standing on its own. The old brickwork alongside where the wheel had turned was marked with lime-scale where the water had splashed. Above this was new brickwork, right up to the roof. The "LONGFORD 1859" stone tablet which used to be on the house had now been built into this new wall – to mislead future investigators.

I heard that the place had been sold to developers in 1986 and, when I last paid it a visit, in January 1988, it was part of a large construction site. Where the building had stood was a mass of mud and builders' debris, with absolutely nothing to show that a mill had ever existed there.

Whitley Mill, Chevening
(See also p.49 & 50)

Between Riverhead and Otford several small streams join the river Darent from the south and east. The first is the Dibden stream, which rises in wooded country on the northern slope of Bayley's Hill. Within a short distance, in Whitley Forest, it was sufficiently important to have powered a corn mill. This was known as Whitley Mill, or Dibden Mill, and, somewhat surprisingly, was just within the parish of Chevening. It appears to have ceased work before 1900 and, being a wooden building in a relatively remote location, it would have deteriorated fairly rapidly.

It was in September 1955 when I visited the site. The overgrown pond was easily recognisable and, on the other side of the track across the dam, was a modern brick water tank. Conveying a trickle of water from an iron pipe into this tank, I was amazed to see, was the unmistakable cast-iron pentrough, 27 inches wide, for an overshot waterwheel! Of the mill itself, absolutely nothing remained.

The area was very overgrown, but one further discovery was to be made. In the bed of the stream, a little below the site of the mill were the remains of a heavy wooden shaft. It was 9 feet 6 inches long, with an iron cross-tailed gudgeon, held by a pair of rings, at each end. About half of the length was 18 inches square and the remainder was circular, of about 12 inches diameter. There were no mortises in the shaft for the arms of wooden gears. The conclusion that this was the wheel-shaft was not confirmed until many years later when a photograph of the wheel turned up which showed some of the details I had measured.

Bradbourne Mill, Sevenoaks
(See also p.51)

The same stream flows down northwards from Dibden to join the Darent about half a mile below the site of Longford Mill. Just before it passes under the main road from Riverhead to Sevenoaks, it feeds an attractive pond in Bradbourne Park. This is thought to be the site of the ancient Bradbourne Mill, which probably disappeared about 300 years ago.

Greatness Corn Mill, Sevenoaks *(See also p.52)*

The next stream began as a spring-fed pond at Greatness, just north of the main road from Riverhead to Seal. This site appears to go back at least to the 14th century. On a visit in April 1953, accompanied by my father, part of a small choked pond still contained some water, perched above a lofty, five-storeyed, weatherboarded mill building. The area between the present pond and the mill had clearly once been a second, larger pond, but was now occupied by a couple of early 20th century corrugated iron buildings. The tall roadside mill building with its lucomb was attractive, but did not have the appearance of age shown by other mills in the district.

Venturing inside, I found a friendly man who told me

Chipstead Mill, Chevening. Site of waterwheel; Alan Stoyel, 2nd May 1954

The site of the waterwheel from downstream. The mill is on the right, with some ragstone incorporated into the brick-work, and the brick mill house is on the left. The head-race used to be at a higher level and the waterwheel was overshot.

the place had been burnt down after the First World War. The mill was then rebuilt, powered by electricity, and the waterwheel was scrapped. He showed me the rubbish-filled pit at the South end of the building where the wheel had once been. Part of the smashed-off cast-iron pentrough for an overshot waterwheel was still there, cemented in place, so I was able to measure the size of the former wheel – which had been approximately 20 feet diameter by 4 feet wide.

Beneath the boarded stone-floor two bedstones were still in place, along the upstream side of the mill, suggesting a lay-shaft drive off a spur-geared pitwheel. Since the waterwheel appeared to have been an overshot one, if there had been a lay-shaft drive to the millstones, it should have been on the downstream side of the mill, working off the loaded side of the waterwheel. It is likely, therefore, that the layout was completely changed when the mill was rebuilt, and that these millstones were only set up in this configuration when electricity had become the power source. The millstone nearer to the site of the waterwheel could be seen to be a composition stone, suggesting the production of animal feed – a likely late use for the mill. Along the roadside bank, a few yards down from the mill, was a fine row of eight old millstones, mostly French burr stones, but including composition stones by Barron & Son Ltd. of Gloucester.

Subsequent research confirmed that the mill had been powered by a 20-foot overshot waterwheel, and that this was driving two pairs of French burrs and one pair of Peaks in 1891, when the mill was for sale.[29] By 1906 the mill had allegedly been fitted with roller plant, and the width of the waterwheel was given as 4½ feet.[30] Despite the stated roller mill installation, and the verbal information that the mill had been gutted by fire soon after the First World War, sale particulars in 1927[31] show the building then contained three pairs of stones, still powered by the waterwheel, aided by a 15 horse-power gas engine. The sequence of events is somewhat puzzling, but it is most likely that the fire, and the subsequent rebuilding, occurred in, or very shortly after, 1927.

Greatness Silk Mill, Sevenoaks

(See also p.54)

Mill Lane followed approximately the course of the stream below Greatness corn mill, and then turned a sharp bend by some rag-stone cottages. Nearby was the site of the famous Greatness silk mill. Of this nothing remains, although these cottages were almost certainly associated with it. The silk mill produced crepe silk and

was built in the mid 18th century, probably on the site of a former fulling mill.[32] It closed in about 1828,[33] and was demolished, but has become immortalised in a long verse by Joseph Harrison entitled "Ode on the Silk Mills at Greatness".[34]

Childs Bridge Mill, Kemsing

(See also p.54)

This site of a presumed corn mill is on the border between the parishes of Kemsing and Seal. It lies on the small stream, known locally as the Guzzlebrook, which rises at Heaverham and flows westwards along the broad Gault Clay valley to join the Darent close to its confluence with the stream from Greatness. Nothing is known of the history of this mill, the former existence of which was first recognised in 1927.[35]

The mill appears to have stood at the lowest point of Childsbridge Lane, which runs from the west end of Kemsing to Seal. When I first visited the site, on a cold April morning in 1954 the marshy outline of the mill pond could be seen to the east, even though the area had been drained. The pond appeared to have been considerable, about 400 yards long and 50 yards wide, and some low revetted banks were in evidence. There were remnants of masonry footings, but there was nothing diagnostic of a watermill. The available head was limited, suggesting that a waterwheel here would have been breast-shot rather than overshot.

Returning in October 1965 with my father, we found further drainage works had been carried out, and the whole mill pond area was under cultivation. There was still some flint masonry debris in evidence near the road, but the confines of the former pond had been ploughed out and were no longer visible. Even in such a rural location, what traces there had been of this mill site eleven years previously had virtually disappeared.

Longlodge Mill, Otford

Here was another likely mill site, further down the Guzzlebrook, which was only identified as such in 1964.[36] The field evidence consisted of a North-South embankment across the valley, apparently retaining quite a large former pond, but with no sign of any associated building. There is a possibility this could be one of the eight mills recorded in the Domesday Book for the Manor of Otford. Certainly the absence of any local knowledge regarding a mill here, as well as the lack of field-name evidence, suggests its early abandonment. The site was on the line of

Longford Mill, Otford. The mill from upstream. Alan Stoyel, 24th April 1956

The dry leat is in the foreground, and the headrace is the dark opening below the brick-work of the mill house to the left. The very wide overshot waterwheel was immediately below one of the main rooms of the house, and it was hardly surprising that there were times when the pictures would rattle on the walls. All has now gone.

Longford Mill, Otford. The front of the mill. Alan Stoyel, 7th August 1966

The front of the mill has had the upper windows and most of the weatherboarding replaced, and the tail-race channel in-filled, although the tail-race arch is still open with the waterwheel in-side at this time. This makes an interesting comparison with the next illustration.

Longford Mill, Otford. The Front of the mill. Local newspaper cutting, early 20th century

A picture of the mill in its working days, with the overshot wheel turning and a cart at the door. The mill is shown as it had been rebuilt in 1859, and the extended gable end indicates a lucomb used to be there on the left-hand end of the building.

Below: Whitley Mill, Chevening. Trough feeding water tank. Alan Stoyel, 15th September 1955

The waterwheel pit has been rebuilt as a brick water tank, but, feeding water into the tank, was still the old cast-iron pentrough which once fed the waterwheel of Whitley Mill. This, and the old wooden wheelshaft lying in the stream nearby, were all that survived of the mill by that time. It was the detailing of this cast-ironwork, and of the wooden shaft, which enabled the following photograph to be identified!

Opposite bottom: Longford Mill, Otford. The site of the mill and house. Alan Stoyel, 21st January 1988

This view is very similar to the one in the previous photograph, but the two images could hardly show a greater contrast.

Bradbourne Mill, Sevenoaks. The former mill pond; Alan Stoyel, 21st January 1988

This is an ancient site, although a mill has probably not stood here since the 17th century. The pond is now a feature of the public park, and it has seen many alterations over the centuries. It serves as a reminder that here was another of those once important mills which were formerly powered by a tributary of the River Darent.

Opposite page: Whitley Mill, Chevening. The mill in working condition.
Photographer unknown, c.1890s.
[Copyright National Monuments Record, ref. no. BB98/22759]

A wonderful photograph of the overshot waterwheel, showing the header-tank and pentrough which have been retained in the later water tank. The building appears to be completely of wooden construction, except for a very small area of brick-work immediately alongside the wheel. The shaft and shrouds of the wheel are of wood, although the arms are of cast-iron, and the buckets appear to be of iron as well.

Greatness Corn Mill, Sevenoaks. The mill from the southeast. Derek Stoyel, 4th April 1953

The large weatherboarded mill which was totally rebuilt in the late 1920s. The corrugated-iron buildings to the left were presumably built on the site of the former mill pond at about the same time. Still visible on the mill roof is the painted "MELDAN AND DRINKWATER", recalling the cabinet-makers and upholsterers who occupied the building after milling had ceased. The rag-stone base of the mill is probably of late 18th century date.

the projected M26 motorway route, and so, once again, little, if any, evidence is likely to survive now.

Otford Mill *(See also p.55 & 57)*

The next mill on the main river was another corn mill which I never saw. A large weatherboarded building spanning the river, it had been destroyed by fire, almost thirty years previously. It used to have two waterwheels, and was, as far as is known, the highest mill in the course of the River Darent to have more than a single wheel. This had long been the arrangement, as, even in medieval times, it was described as two mills under one roof.[37] From sale particulars of 1837 comes a most interesting and detailed description of the mill.[38] At that time there were six pairs of stones driven by the two iron breast-shot waterwheels. The western wheel had a wooden shaft and drove three pairs of French burr and a pair of Peak stones through wooden machinery. The eastern wheel powered two pairs of French stones with new iron machinery. A further point of interest was the suggestion made of deepening the tailrace to increase the available head, which would enable the breast-shot waterwheels to be replaced by overshot ones, thus increasing the power. This modification was never carried out.

A single-storeyed dwelling had been erected, straddling the river, on the site of part of the former mill building. A 42-inch diameter Peak millstone could be seen, acting as the sole reminder of the scale of the industry which once existed in what had become such tranquil and mature riverside gardens.

I learnt that the mill had caught fire in January 1924, a little before midnight. The blaze was believed to have started in a pile of sawdust. At that time use of the mill was shared between Mr. Baker, who was a joiner, and Mr. Freeman, the owner, who had an engineering workshop there. They both used the remaining waterwheel to generate power for their machines. Nothing could be done to save the building.

Shoreham Corn Mill
(See also p.58, 59 & 61)

Shoreham was an attractive village which I knew quite well, but it was a source of puzzlement to me. Here was an ancient village, nestling in the valley of a well-utilised river, but where was the source of its flour? Eventually I found it, half a mile upstream. It turned out to be the most beautiful little rural watermill I had seen; a squat building with tiled cat-slide roof, pierced by dormers, above a low wall of twisted elm weatherboards. The mill was first viewed across a pool immediately below the bypass sluice, where the white water cascaded, before ambling gently round in the clear pool, appreciated by a large number of fish. The pond above the mill was full of water, and the mill from this upstream side was just as memorable.

On a later visit, when I was 15, I found the mill door open, and, since there was nobody about, I ventured inside. I found the internal breast-shot waterwheel had been replaced by a horizontal turbine, which was apparently still used from time to time to drive a circular saw. Originally, through a mortise spurwheel engaging iron stone nuts, it had powered two pairs of millstones – one French burr and one Peak. All of this was still in position. The millstones were on the first floor, but long out of use, and covered with dust. The fittings were complete, with iron hoppers and tuns, wood and iron horses and wooden shoes. To find a complete set of matching stone-furniture like this was indeed rare, and I had never seen iron tuns and hoppers before.

The internal waterwheel must once have been of the order of fourteen feet in diameter by five or six feet wide. The millstones were not where they would have been when powered by the waterwheel, and the whole mechanical arrangement had been altered when the turbine was installed. The spurwheel driving them was only 39 inches in diameter. I was about to investigate if any evidence remained of the earlier set-up when, through the window, I saw somebody approaching, and beat a hasty

Opposite bottom: Greatness Corn Mill, Sevenoaks. A French burrstone. Alan Stoyel, 21st January 1988

French burr millstones are made up with carefully selected cut blocks of chert, a flinty sedimentary stone, quarried in the Paris basin. The stone was brought over by boat and made up into millstones in various places in England. An iron band around the stone locked the blocks in place, with nothing between these but plaster of Paris. This is a runner stone, as shown by the two recesses in the eye, where the iron bridge was fixed by which the stone was hung on top of the driving spindle. The pattern of furrows in the grinding face can be clearly seen. To have seven radial segments like this is rare; a millstone of this type is generally made up of many more, smaller blocks of stone. Here the iron band has rusted away, so that complete collapse is inevitable.

Greatness Silk Mill, Sevenoaks. Cottages in Mill Lane. Derek Stoyel, 24th October 1969

Nothing remained of the famous silk mill except this row of cottages beside Mill Lane. The formal symmetry of the main elevation, with its central pediment, is an indication that the cottages were part of a grand design, an accompaniment to the nearby textile mill. They are solidly constructed of Kentish rag-stone, the hard, silty limestone which forms the high ground on which Sevenoaks is built.

Childs Bridge Mill, Kemsing. Site of mill and pond. Derek Stoyel, 5th March 1966

This view is looking across the site of the mill pond from the NW corner. Childsbridge Lane, on the right, probably follows the line of the mill dam across the Guzzlebrook stream, which flows from left to right. By this time the area of the former mill pond had been drained and was under cultivation.

Otford Mill, from upstream. Photographer unknown, pre-1924.

A view of the mill from where the private drive left the main road, beside the bridge. The long weather-boarded front of the mill runs across the whole width of the impounded water.

Otford Mill, from upstream. Derek Stoyel, 24th October 1965

The same view of the mill over 40 years later. The mill has been replaced by a modern bungalow, occupying part of the same site. Apart from its surroundings being more manicured, and the water level reduced, nothing else has changed.

retreat.

It was seven years before I returned. The sight that greeted me was like a nightmare. The undulating boarding, the long russet slope of the roof, the delicate traditional wooden-framed windows – all had gone! The beautiful old building had become a modern house, regimented slats and picture windows were now surmounted by clinical tiles and rooflights – all protected by a palisade of scaffolding poles. Was there no justice in a planning system designed to protect such traditional and historic gems. Having already experienced the destruction of the wonderful mill at Westerham, I now realised that it was not just an isolated case. I was at a loss to understand how such acts of vandalism could be condoned, particularly when both victims were such particular favourites of mine! I realised that the few surviving watermills in West Kent were all severely at risk.

Shoreham Paper Mill

(See also p.61 & 63)

This mill was at the Northern end of the village, on a short leat, to the West side of the River Darent. The attractive mill house, of brick and white weatherboarding, was occupied. I knocked on the door one April morning in 1954 and the owner showed me where the mill had once stood. A concrete weir had been built where the old bypass sluices used to be, but the brick wheel-race was still there in the garden. It was in perfect condition, as if waiting for its wheel to be returned to it. There had been a low-breast waterwheel here, approximately 16 feet in diameter by 8 feet wide, with the water entry about 3 feet below the wheelshaft centre. The machinery it had driven was formerly on the Eastern side of the wheel, and the evidence suggested this had been by a lay-shaft drive from a spur-geared pitwheel.

The owner, who had not been there very long, could only tell me that the mill had been demolished in the 1930s after a spell of disuse, although the waterwheel was left untouched for some years until that, too, was removed before the 1939-45 war. I later learnt that it was in 1930 that the mill had been pulled down, and that the bricks and tiles had been salvaged and re-used in a house called "Tilemans Field" at Farningham.[39] By an amazing chance, nearly fifty years after my visit to the site, I was able to obtain a photograph of the old waterwheel taken by a fellow mill enthusiast from Wiltshire.

The mill had previously been a fulling mill in the 17th century. The transition from fulling to papermaking is often to be found in Kent paper mills. Hand-made paper had been produced here for over 200 years, for most of which time this was by various members of the Wilmot family. In particular the speciality was in paper for government department ledgers.[40] It was said, too, that it was paper from this mill which was the first to be exported from England to arrive at its destination without having developed mildew.[41]

Wood Mill, Eynsford

Nothing is left of this sawmill, which formerly stood close to the Lullingstone Roman villa site which has now become so famous. It is possible that an ancient mill site had been redeveloped, as Hasted mentions the existence of a mill at Lullingstone soon after the Domesday survey, although that is much more likely to have stood further upstream. The sawmill itself was not an ancient one, having been newly erected in 1853.[42] Twelve years later it was referred to as "Wood Mill" by a local angler.[43] I looked for any remnant of this mill on more than one occasion, but without success. The lack of field evidence for any significant engineering work having been carried out supports the conclusion that this is not an ancient mill site.

Old Mill, Eynsford (See also p.64 & 65)

This enigmatic building stands adjacent to the popular bridge and ford which form the focal point of the village. The strange thing about this building is that it stands immediately <u>down</u>stream of the ancient ford – a most illogical and impractical location. Wondering if this mill had really ever been water powered, I talked to the owner of the "Old Mill" on a return visit to Kent in 1976, and explained my puzzlement. He could not supply any information, but willingly allowed me to go wherever I wanted.

That the building had formerly been a mill was soon abundantly clear. Not only were there three millstones set in the ground outside, but I found there had once been a loading door, now covered with weatherboarding, over the present front door of the house. When I crawled in the river under the building I found plenty of evidence that a waterwheel had worked here. There were scratch marks where the wheel had scraped the wall, the curved cast-iron guides for the penstock were still in place on each side, and there was a dressed stone sill, where the water once entered the waterwheel. This sill was visible as a small step in the river bed. Upstream of the sill the bed of the river was flush with it. On the downstream side, however, it was low enough to expose the top few

Otford Mill, from downstream. Commercial postcard, pre-1924

This photograph shows the size of the building and also the three watercourses beneath it, two of which contained waterwheels. One of the men standing to the right of the mill is holding the blade of a circular saw – presumably this was one of the pieces of equipment being driven by the remaining waterwheel at this time.

Otford Mill, from downstream. Photographer unknown, January 1924.

A similar view to the last, taken just after the fire, showing how complete the destruction from the fire had been. Such a dangerous structure would not have been left standing like this for long. Clearly there was precious little that could be salvaged from the remains.

Shoreham Corn Mill, from the bypass stream. Anthony Stoyel, late 1960s.

The beautiful weatherboarded building with its wonderful tiled roof, viewed from the north. The water in the foreground is cascading over the bypass sluice. The tailrace from the internal turbine ran beneath the bushes to the left of this photograph.

Shoreham Corn Mill from the bypass stream. Derek Stoyel, 16th June 1971

The unsympathetic conversion of the mill is now in full swing.

Shoreham Corn Mill from the bypass stream. Alan Stoyel, 15th May 1976

The final sad result - a modern house, showing little resemblance to the original.

Shoreham Corn Mill, viewed from upstream. Alan Stoyel, 11th September 1954

An idyllic scene of the mill standing at the end of its pond. The railings in the foreground follow the curve of the pond to the bypass sluice, just to the left of the building. The headrace to the turbine is beneath the wooden railings in front of the mill.

inches of curved breastwork below the water. Where the bottom couple of feet of the wheel had once been, was now below the river bed. Above my head, the area once occupied by the waterwheel had been floored over, and was now part of the living room. The wheel had been 10 feet wide, and I had estimated its diameter as being at least 10 feet. Subsequently I found that, in 1885, a waterwheel here had been advertised for sale as being only 8 feet in diameter[44]. This surprised me, but I have not yet gone back into the river to check my estimate!

A prominent feature of the building was the corrugated iron roof, semicircular in profile. Previously I had imagined it to have been a relatively recent adaptation. When I investigated the loft, however, I found old, limewashed, arched timber trusses, respecting the symmetry of the 9 feet radius of the semicircular iron sheeting. Each arch was tensioned by a pair of vertical tie-rods which were attached to longitudinal timbers below the floor boarding. I had not seen a construction of this type, and clearly the roof was much older than I had thought. Additional evidence came when I looked at the quality of the corrugated iron, which was superior to anything I had noticed before. The owner had said that he was hoping to change the roof for something more conventional and, in his eyes, more attractive. While I was there a squall of heavy rain came by and I began to understand the owner's desire to change the roof material, as the noise in the loft was deafening!

Many years later I saw a photograph of an 1887 painting published in a magazine,[45] showing the mill in the background, already with its curved roof, which vindicated the field evidence. The mill itself is still something of a mystery. Despite its unusual siting, just below a ford, the statutory Listing schedule described it as an 18th century corn mill on the site of an earlier mill. Surely no mill could have been constructed until at least a bridge provided an alternative to the ford, and current thinking seems to put the age of the bridge at the 17th century – so any mill at this location should post-date that. All three millstones are only 36 inches in diameter, which suggests that power was limited – as indeed could only be expected in this situation. Directory references show the mill operating as a corn mill until about 1911, and that water, alone, was still providing the power. Did the waterwheel advertised in 1885 not attract a buyer, or was it superseded by a replacement, perhaps of a larger diameter? After milling had ceased, the building was used for a short time as a bootlace-packing shop, employing local girls, but it soon became empty, and was eventually converted to a dwelling in the early 1920s.

Opposite top: Shoreham Corn Mill, the stone furniture inside the mill. Alan Stoyel, 11th September 1954

This photograph, taken with my box camera propped-up in the semi-darkness, is a poor one, but is almost certainly unique. At the bottom of the picture is the circular galvanised steel tun around one of the two pairs of millstones. The horse, hopper, shoe and damsel can be made out. The slim iron upright shaft is visible near the right-hand margin of the picture, and there is a second matching set of stone furniture beyond it.

Opposite bottom: Shoreham Paper Mill. The mill house from upstream. Alan Stoyel, May 1956

The only remaining member of the paper mill complex, this house stands between the site of the mill and the river Darent. It is a very interesting building with a complex history, and is thought to incorporate a medieval framed structure. It appears to have been remodelled in the early nineteenth century.

Eynsford Paper Mill (See also p.66)

Originally a corn mill, in 1648 this site became one of the earliest paper mills to be established in Kent. It continued in the same use until it closed in 1952,[46] although the historic buildings had been totally destroyed by two serious fires within about a year of 1907. When I was investigating the mills on the Darent, Eynsford Paper Mill was a modern factory, apparently with nothing of interest except a weir and a short leat. The place had little more appeal than any other such factory, and I never investigated it. When I returned to see the site in 1986, the whole complex had been completely demolished quite recently. The headrace was still full of water, which was pouring over the spillway, and the course of the former tailrace could still be made out. The difference in water level between the two races must have been at least 7 feet, which, in earlier days, when the flow was so much greater, would have constituted a significant source of power. In 1882 the iron waterwheel, presumably a breast wheel, was advertised for sale. It measured 18 feet 3 inches in diameter by 8 feet wide.[47]

Farningham Mill (See also p.67)

Perhaps the most beautiful mill in Kent, it proved to be the county's most bitter disappointment for me. Having

had such kind receptions from all the owners and occupiers of mills over recent months I entered the front gate of the property and walked up to a man who was standing a few yards up the drive. Briefly I explained my quest and asked permission to have a closer look at the mill. He refused. Replying to my quizzical expression he countered: "I don't let anyone else; why should I let you?" Try as I might, he would not relent, not even allowing me to approach any closer in order to take a photograph. I was forced to acknowledge defeat, and to retreat. I fumed with self-righteous indignation. At fifteen, this was the first such rebuff I had received, and, in the very few times since then that I have been refused access to a mill, only once has the effect it produced in me been exceeded. Over fifty years later, I have yet to try to investigate Farningham Mill again!

A traditional site, the present mill dates from 1790, with milling having ceased in 1900.[48] A turbine has superseded the waterwheel and this was later used to drive a saw. I understand the mill has been gutted of its working parts, but precisely what remains, in terms of artefacts and evidence, is still unknown to me.

Franks Generating Station, Horton Kirby and South Darenth (See also p.68)

Franks is a large, brick-built Elizabethan country house of some distinction, and I had heard rumours of there having been some use of water power inside the grounds. Eventually, in July 1960, my curiosity caused me to trespass within the grounds to find out. What I found was an unattractive brick building of probable late 19th century date, derelict and in ruins, spanning an artificial water channel. This leat was a branch of the Darent, to the East of the main river, but it had been blocked off just upstream of the structure. The site was wooded, and a tree had fallen across the walls of the building, adding to the desolation. It appeared to have been a purpose-built power-house for electricity generation, but all the working parts had clearly been removed a long time before. My conclusion was that the power had been derived from an internal turbine, and that a waterwheel had not preceded it –at least not in the present structure. I learnt later that this was indeed a generating station which had supplied Franks with electricity until the mains supply was brought in. The turbine from here is reputed to be the one which still survives at the site of Westminster Mill, the next mill downstream.[49]

Westminster Mill, Horton Kirby and South Darenth

(See also p.69)

Westminster Mill was one of those rather dismal factory-like mills, so typical of the fringes of London. The unrelieved formality of its fenestration and general form, the smoke-grimed yellow of the three storeys of stock brick, and the unrelenting roof of patent tiles all conspired to dispel the belief that watermills were always attractive. The Darent, rippling over the wide spillway, did its best to improve the place. Just as the scene contrasted so markedly with that of Farningham Mill, so did the reception I received. Not only did the man I accosted give me all the help he could, but various informants who had connections with the mill kindly continued to supply me with information for months after my visit.

At that time, in September 1954, a horizontal turbine was still in place in a yellow brick extension of the mill. This had been in use here, generating electricity, up until the beginning of the 1939-45 war, towards the end in conjunction with a Petters oil engine.[50] Originally a

Opposite top: Shoreham Paper Mill, the wheel-race. Alan Stoyel, 15th May 1976

A view of the wheel-race from downstream, showing the curved breast-work of brick where the waterwheel used to be. The wheel was low breast-shot, approximately 16 feet in diameter by 8 feet wide, with the centre of the wheel-shaft about 36 inches above the top of the breast-work.

Opposite bottom: Shoreham Paper Mill, the derelict waterwheel. A.E. Bancroft, About 1936.

In the foreground is the brick wall-base of the recently-demolished mill building. The waterwheel is mostly of cast-iron, with wooden starts and floats. Each of the three rings has been cast integrally with the arms, but in halves. Each casting is thus a semicircle, with three complete arms and half of each of two others. When each pair of semi-circles is bolted together, the joint runs down the middle of one arm and continues down the middle of the arm's opposite number on the other side. The bolted joints can be seen in the photograph, on all three of the inclined arms on the left-hand side.

Top: Old Mill, Eynsford. The mill from upstream. Alan Stoyel, May 1956

In the foreground is the ford, with the eastern part of the historic bridge. The end bay of the mill building, in line with the first arch, was a bypass channel. The waterwheel occupied the second bay, behind the bridge abutment in this view.

Left: Old Mill, Eynsford. The front door. Alan Stoyel, 8th September 1988

The front door appears to have been made narrower when the building was converted into a cottage, and one of the millstones, a 36-inch French burr, has been set in the ground outside. Above the front door can be seen a vertical joint in the weatherboarding, marking the left-hand jamb of the mill loading door.

Old Mill, Eynsford. The site of the waterwheel. Alan Stoyel, 8th September 1988

The brick wheel-race beneath the building, looking east, with the river flowing from right to left. Part of the curved, iron penstock guide is visible, running down into the water, with some scratch-marks from the former low breast-shot waterwheel now infilled with cement.

flour mill had stood here, and the well-known Cannon family had this and South Darenth Mill before taking on Old Mill, Bexley, and, finally, the huge steam roller-mill at Erith. Westminster Mill was destroyed by fire in 1879, but was rebuilt. It was converted to roller milling in 1894, driven by a breast wheel and a steam engine,[51] but grinding ceased in 1899, at which time it claimed to have been the last working flour mill on the river Darent.[52] The mill then turned to the production of electric batteries, but was burnt to the ground again in about 1910.[53] Most of the building which was visible in 1954 had been the result of the ensuing rebuilding – as a turbine-driven flour mill once more. This venture was short-lived, however, and from 1914 onwards the mill had been used to produce shoe accessories.[54]

When I visited the mill again, in September 1975, the buildings had gone out of use, and part had been gutted by yet another fire. A tiny waterwheel could be seen on the south side of the spillway, however. Apparently this was coupled to a sluice control mechanism, so that the retained water was kept automatically at a constant level in the pond.

In September 2007 I returned to find the mill had gone, replaced by a new housing development on the east bank of the Darent called "Millen Court", presumably in memory of the family who were the last owners of the mill – Walter Millen had been one of those who had been so helpful to me over 50 years before. Despite the complete absence of the former industrial buildings, the spillway and the base of the turbine house had survived. The turbine, reputed to have come from the powerhouse at Franks[55], is still in place here, where a waterwheel had worked for at least five hundred years.

Horton Kirby Paper Mills, Horton Kirby and South Darenth

Ever since I had known them, Horton Kirby Paper Mills were a large, impenetrable factory complex, dominated by an enormous brick chimney. The paper mill had been

Eynsford Paper Mill. View looking southeast. Alan Stoyel, 14th May 1956

This is a distant view of the complex, with its attendant housing, seen from the valley side to the west. Any historic structure would have disappeared as a result of devastating fires at the beginning of the twentieth century.

Eynsford Paper Mill. The bypass sluice. Alan Stoyel 1st August 1986

The whole papermaking complex has been demolished and the redevelopment of the site is now virtually complete. In the foreground is the old bypass sluice, with the impounded water in the background. This sluice could be opened up if the water level needed to be reduced – either for repairs to be carried out, or at times of flood. Beyond it, the patch of weeds marks where the headrace once ran to feed the waterwheel.

founded by John Hall, the eminent Dartford engineer, in about 1820 on the site of a former corn mill.[56] The Darent flowed through the centre of the complex and was probably utilised for power in the early days of papermaking here, although later it was presumably used only as process water. Over the years the works had been expanded and modernised, so that little of interest remained. The site was close to an elevated stretch of railway line, and I used to be fascinated by the view of densely-packed buildings which was afforded to passengers on the passing train, although I never ventured inside the gates. The most impressive feature was the brick chimney, displaying its 1880 date so proudly. This had been extended incongruously, with no deference to the previous design, and formed a unique landmark, visible for miles.

I passed the site in September 2007 and found the whole complex was a scene of dereliction, and the majority of buildings had already been demolished. The enormous brick chimney remained, however, all the more impressive in its relative isolation. Although it was a Listed Building I wondered how long it would survive.

Between the village of Horton Kirby and the town of Dartford the Darent valley is flatter and more mature, and the river itself splits into a series of channels. There have been mills on both the main streams, the western one serving Sutton at Hone and the eastern supplying the village of Darenth. Largely spring fed, the western

stream had developed sufficiently to have powered Frog Lane Mill in parallel with Horton Kirby Paper Mills

Frog Lane Mill, Sutton at Hone *(See also p.71-73)*

This mill stood about a quarter of a mile west of Horton Kirby Paper Mills. Only the bottom storey of the building remained when I visited it in August 1953, although the little pent-roofed wheelhouse on the western side still contained its waterwheel. My attention to this mill had been drawn by Mr. Philip Street a few months before, when he had kindly given me a print of his photograph of the mill, taken in 1928. Later, in February 1936, he had seen the upper part of the building being demolished.

The mill and a pair of cottages stood on the north side of Frog Lane. To the south, the millpond had once extended back as far as the railway, but this was now bone-dry, as were the old watercourses at the mill itself. The place was dead and sterile, having lost its life force. The ground floor wall of the mill was still standing, in yellow brick, probably of early 19th century date. The rest, of weatherboarding, had all been removed. The waterwheel was easy of access and mostly in good condition. It was a shrouded, completely iron, breast wheel measuring exactly 10 feet in diameter and 6 feet wide. Of late 19th century appearance, it was fed by an iron trough with a curved penstock, but no inscription could be found. The

Farningham Mill. Front of mill, E.J. & W.W. Crow, 26th October 1930

The main view of the mill, with the mill house to the left, as seen from the approach off the village street. It forms a classic watermill image with its mansard roof and central lucomb. The amazing symmetry has been extended by painting a duplicate door, complete with fanlight, on the neat weatherboarding. This mill faces downstream, and the river is re-emerging from the former tailrace and bypass channels beneath the loading-bridge.

Franks Generating Station, Horton Kirby and South Darenth. Alan Stoyel, 10th July 1960

This is a view of the downstream side of the ruined building - a gutted shell in a woodland setting. It was not an easy subject for photography, particularly in Summertime. The tailrace channel is in the foreground.

Franks Generating Station, Horton Kirby and South Darenth. Alan Stoyel, 10th July 1960

A close-up view of the downstream wall showing the desolation of the site, with the remains of a large fallen tree projecting through a former window. The opening where the tailwater used to flow out from the turbine is below the rolled steel joist near the bottom of the picture. Above this is a semicircular arch in the brick-work. Was this an earlier tailrace arch for a waterwheel which was infilled when a turbine was installed? Or was it merely a stress-relieving arch above the rolled steel joist in a single phase of building? I favoured the latter interpretation.

Westminster Mill, Horton Kirby & South Darenth. The mill from upstream. Alan Stoyel, May 1956

This view is looking across the pond, showing not only how large the complex was but how extensive was the mill pond which fed it. The turbine house projects from the main block, and the old square chimney of the steam engine was still standing then.

Westminster Mill, Horton Kirby & South Darenth. The mill from downstream. Alan Stoyel, 23rd June 1988

By this time part of the complex had disappeared, and what remained was abandoned and forlorn. The turbine house, bypass sluice and spillway are still as they had been for generations, but one relatively recent addition was the tiny waterwheel at the left-hand end of the spillway. This wheel was connected to the sluice mechanism and was an attempt at automatic sluice control to deal with fluctuating water conditions. This view is still recognisable today, although all the mill buildings have disappeared.

5 inches square iron wheelshaft still carried a particularly large pitwheel, of the same diameter as the waterwheel. This was bevelled, with wooden cogs, but nothing else survived of the working parts.

I talked to one or two elderly local inhabitants, from whom I gathered that Charles Pike was the last miller. Milling had ceased by the time war broke out in 1914, and towards the end only pig food had been ground. Apparently the millpond used to be a popular place for skating and, on one crowded occasion, Mr. Pike had started up the waterwheel – causing great consternation as the water was withdrawn from beneath the ice!

When I returned in June 1965 I found the waterwheel and wheelhouse had been completely swept away. Where they had stood was now a broad, but dry, canal. Almost the last of the many waterwheels on the Darent had been allowed to go, seemingly without any protest, but.I was greatly saddened by this loss.

South Darenth Flour Mill, Horton Kirby and South Darenth (See also p.74, 76 & 77)

A short distance downstream from the Horton Kirby Paper Mills is a yellow brick building, spanning the eastern branch of the Darent with two shallow arches.

At the time of my visit, in September 1954, it was an electrically-powered sawmill, and a wood-yard occupied the site of the in-filled millpond. Apart from the building's relationship to the river, it exhibited little external evidence of having been a water-powered mill. I was shown around inside, but again there was nothing to be seen of its former use that I could detect. Local enquiries showed the present building had indeed been a flour mill, but that later it had been a roller mill powered by a steam engine. It had been rebuilt following a dramatic fire in 1879[57] which had destroyed the old weatherboarded watermill.

This previous mill was a fine timber building with a mansard roof, occupying the same position as the present structure. Mr. V. H. Thompson, who owned a shop in Sutton at Hone, was kind enough to lend me a faded photograph of the old mill. I had it copied before returning the picture, and it is reproduced here. The mill had three pairs of stones originally,[58] and the iron waterwheel had a beam engine installed in a brick extension as auxiliary power. The chimney of the steam engine survived the fire, and was only taken down in about 1946.[59] This was yet another mill operated by the Cannon family in the past.

Latterly the flour mill was primarily steam-powered, although directories from 1887 until 1903[60] still specified steam and water as the power sources. In 1894 Robinson & Son installed the roller plant of 2½ sacks per hour capacity.[61] Milling did not last very long, however, and had ceased by June 1905, when the mill was sold by auction.[62] The yellow brick dwelling which now occupies the site has been rebuilt from the remains of the eastern part of the post-1879 building, which was damaged severely in the hurricane in October1987.

Darenth Paper Mill, Darenth
(See also p.77 & 78)

This was the next mill on the eastern arm of the river, shortly before the confluence of the two streams. It used to be renowned for the quality of its paper, which was made into bank notes, both in Britain and on the Continent.

My interest in the mill had been stimulated by a 1910 photograph I had seen of a new steam wagon supplied to T.H. Saunders & Co. Ltd., Paper Manufacturers. The wagon bore their name proudly on its side, together with the mills they operated - Hawley & Darenth Mills, Kent and Rye Mill, High Wycombe, Bucks. Unlike other paper mills I had seen, Darenth was a sprawl of generally low buildings, one or two of which looked quite old.

Papermaking ceased in 1931 when this mill, and Hawley Mill downstream, was taken over by Messrs. Portals of Laverstoke, Hampshire.[63] When I visited Darenth Paper Mill in 1954 it was occupied by a flag-making firm, who had been there for about twenty years. There seemed to be very little activity in the place, and a man I accosted was happy to show me where the waterwheel had been. Its former position was clearly visible, and it had been a breast wheel about twelve feet in diameter by approximately ten feet wide. I was told the wheel had been of iron, with wooden floats, and it had been sold for scrap some time before. It had developed a serious imbalance, so that pieces of lead needed to be attached to the arms. Its last task had been to drive a dynamo, coupled to a Blackstone oil engine.

I visited the site in 2007, but found all the buildings had disappeared; only a pile of rubble remained. The only exception was the mill house to the east, beside the road. The whole area of the former mill complex had been cordoned off, and foundations for a new housing development were being dug. The disappearance of the paper mills, for which the Darent was once so famous, has been total.

Frog Lane Mill, Sutton at Hone. Mill and house. Philip Street, 10th November 1928

The mill is seen from upstream, with the small wheelhouse just visible at the far end. To the right is a pair of cottages. Clearly the mill is beginning to deteriorate, and it was demolished just over seven years later.

Frog Lane Mill, Sutton at Hone. The waterwheel. Alan Stoyel, 11th September 1954

The derelict, completely iron, breast-shot waterwheel is in the remnants of the wheelhouse, with the brick base of the mill to the right. To the left of the wheel is the bypass sluice

Frog Lane Mill, Sutton at Hone. The waterwheel. Alan Stoyel, 11th September 1954

The outer bearing of the iron waterwheel, looking through an aperture in the wheelhouse wall. Each set of eight arms was cast as a unit, tailor-made to fit onto the square iron wheel-shaft. The whole arrangement had been constructed in the mid 19th century as a single phase.

Frog Lane Mill, Sutton at Hone. The mill site. Alan Stoyel, 21st August 1964

The water channel has been opened up deepened, and, in the process, the wheelhouse, waterwheel and bypass sluice-way have all been swept away with total disregard of the fact that this was one of the last waterwheels to survive in the whole of the course of the River Darent. This photograph makes an interesting comparison with the photograph on page 71, taken 36 years previously.

South Darenth Flour Mill, from upstream. Derek Stoyel, 8th August 1953

The rebuilt mill astride the river, with the overgrown site of the pond in the foreground.

Sutton Mill, Sutton at Hone

(See also p.78-80)

Sutton Mill occupied a relatively isolated position on the western arm of the river. Its proximity to Darenth Mill, and the fact that the Sutton at Hone/Darenth parish boundary followed the middle of the stream, has caused some confusion in the past, and it has been incorrectly referred to as Old Mill at Darenth, Darenth Corn Mill and Little Darenth Mill. The boundary passed through the centre of the waterwheel, but all the machinery, and hence the historic mill site, was within Sutton at Hone parish.

When I visited the site in 1955, only the brick-lined watercourse could be seen running through the farmyard. Mr. Norton, the farmer, told me a bomb had fallen through the roof in the First World War and put the mill out of action. The building was finally demolished in 1928. Some time later, a home-made waterwheel, constructed from a pair of cartwheels, had been installed in the race,[64] but of this there was no sign.

It had been a most attractive mill, very traditional, with white weatherboards and tiled mansard roof with a gable-end lucomb. As a result, several external views of Sutton Mill survive. Mr. Philip Street wrote to me confirming that the demolition of the mill had been in the Autumn of 1928.[65] He had seen the resulting piles of debris, and could attest to the antiquity of the timbers. Not only was he kind enough to give me his photographs of the wreckage, but also three photographic prints, taken by a Miss Pyefinch of Dartford, of the mill in the process of demolition. These are two of the most exciting pictures in my collection and are reproduced here. They throw an extraordinary amount of light on a mill about which so little is known.

Hawley Paper Mill, Sutton at Hone (See also p.80, 82 & 83)

This was the first mill after the confluence of the two branches of the river. It had been a paper mill from at least 1710.[66] Along with the mill at Darenth it had, until 1931, been occupied by Messrs. T.H. Saunders, making high quality paper for bank-notes and stationery, and gaining a high reputation for the quality of its water-marking.[67]

Like Darenth Paper Mill, this complex consisted of a series of low-key buildings. These were mellow, of red brick and black weatherboarding, and had been occupied since 1936 by Bevington & Sons, leather manufacturers.

When I called there with my father in September 1954 we were greeted warmly by Mr. Wilson, the manager, who took us to see where a pair of waterwheels had once worked, just downstream of the bridge into the complex. They had been low breast-shot wheels, side by side across the main stream, separated only by a narrow bypass channel.

The wheels themselves had been removed, but the river was still running down the curved breastwork, as if to demonstrate how pathetic was the flow compared with the time when these two great wheels were working in parallel. Both waterwheels had been sixteen feet in diameter, but of different widths. The eight-feet wide western one had powered a building on the west bank, but this had long gone, and its site was a mass of shrubs and small trees. On the eastern bank was an attractive two-storeyed building of black weatherboards above brick-work, with a corrugated iron roof topped by a slatted wooden ventilator. The blocked circular shaft-hole into this building from the five-feet wide eastern wheel was clearly visible, but no internal evidence was to be seen of the machinery it had driven.

We were told by Mr. Wilson that the smaller wheel was used to drive a dynamo when Bevington & Sons took over, but was scrapped in the 1939-45 war. Apparently there was once a third waterwheel at the mill, fed by a two-feet-wide aqueduct. It was still there in 1936, but was removed soon afterwards, leaving no trace.

I returned to the site in March 1987 to find the complex had disappeared completely. An ugly single-storeyed concrete building had replaced the attractive weatherboards and brickwork on the eastern bank, and the course of the river had been canalised inside grim concrete walls. A hardly-noticeable step in the river bed marked the position where the penstocks and bypass sluice used to be. However, the brickwork of the eastern side of the eastern wheel-race had been incorporated in the river walling, and there, on the brickwork, the ghostly scratch-marks from the narrower of the two waterwheels were still plainly visible!

Dartford Powder Mills, Wilmington and Dartford

(See also p.83)

This was a large and important complex about a mile upstream of the town, operating from about 1730 until the beginning of the 20th century, with a series of water-powered mills. The development of these is thought

South Darenth Flour Mill, from downstream. Unknown photographer, pre-1882

A view from the northeast of the fine mill which was burnt down in 1881. The chimney of the auxiliary steam engine is visible over the mansard roof. This is from a print which was kindly lent to me by Mr. V.H. Thompson.

Opposite bottom: Darenth Paper Mill, from upstream. Alan Stoyel,
25th January 1961

By this time much of the complex had gone, and little of significance remained. The building seen here was relatively modern, but the internal wheel-race did still survive. This photograph makes an interesting comparison with the next one.

South Darenth Flour Mill. From downstream. Alan Stoyel, 23rd June 1988

This picture makes an interesting comparison with the previous one. Damage to the building from the hurricane of October 1987 was still all too apparent.

Darenth Paper Mill, from upstream. Commercial postcard, pre-1913.

At this time the complex still had character and atmosphere, with a fine square chimney, and a cloud of steam rising from one of the buildings. The pond was wider, and well maintained. The range of buildings is in complete contrast to the scene in the previous photograph. The only structure to survive now is the large Mill House- here seen as the second building from the right.

Sutton Mill, Sutton at Hone, from upstream. Commercial postcard, pre-1919.

This very attractive little mill, with its mansard roof and lucomb, is clearly in good condition, with the pond full of water. The adjoining house is much older and more extensive than this view suggests.

Sutton Mill, Sutton at Hone, from upstream. Mr. Widdows, 1st August 1928

This picture of the mill shows the damage caused by a bomb which came through the roof in the First World War. It makes a sad comparison with the previous view. This was a print given to me by Philip Street from a borrowed negative.

Sutton Mill, Sutton at Hone. The waterwheel. Miss Pyefinch, c28th September 1928

A fascinating photograph of the waterwheel, viewed from upstream, after nearly all the rest of the mill had been removed. At the bottom of the picture is the ribbed shaft for controlling the water to the wheel, the

toothed rack and pinion being in the bottom right-hand corner. The wheel has 3 sets of 6 cast-iron arms and rings, on a circular iron shaft. The floats, and most of the wooden starts, have been smashed off. Weights have been attached to the arms, trying to correct an imbalance in rotation, suggesting that maintenance latterly had become a bit rough and ready. The cross, cut in the timber in the foreground, marks the parish boundary, running through the centre of the waterwheel. Sutton at Hone is to the left and Darenth to the right. The machinery driven by the wheel was to the left – in the parish laying claim to the mill.

Opposite top: Sutton Mill, Sutton at Hone. The machinery. Miss Pyefinch, c.28th September 1928

Another amazing photograph showing the machinery to the west of the waterwheel. A large pitwheel drove a pair of layshafts, the upstream one to a single pair of stones and the downstream one to two pairs – all French burrs. Also powered off the pitwheel was the massive wooden upright shaft with a fine wooden clasp-armed crown-wheel at the top for driving the ancillary machinery. This arrangement is an unusual one, and would never have been suspected if this picture had not survived. This photograph, and the one on p.79, were in the form of small sepia prints, kindly given to me by Philip Street over 50 years ago, and much treasured.

Opposite bottom: Hawley Mill, Sutton-at-Hone. The eastern mill building. Derek Stoyel, 16th September 1954

This is the view looking northeast across the headrace from the bridge, over the western arm of the Darent, which formed the entrance to the works. The building, an attractive mixture of dark weatherboarding and red brick, was formerly powered by

to have incorporated the site of the famous paper mill erected in 1588 by John Spilman. The remains of a couple of the powder mills were partially excavated in 1984 and are still visible on the wooded site.

In July 1954 when I was looking for what remained of these mills the ground on which they stood was strictly private, and for once I was not guilty of trespass. At that time nobody seemed to know what, if anything, survived. If I had found the remains I do not know how much I would have been able to see, let alone interpret, as the area was very overgrown. Also the features were complex and I was unfamiliar with powder mills. At the downstream end of the site, beside a minor road I did find a two-storeyed building of yellow brick with red brick details, then occupied by Lingall Bros. & Co. It was situated between two parallel streams, one at a higher elevation than the other and, connecting the two streams, and adjacent to the building, was a concrete-lined channel controlled by an iron sluice. This channel was probably no more than a bypass for the paper mill site downstream.

However, painted on the door, was "DIRTYSIDE No Employee May Use this Entrance When Wearing Magazine Clothing", so the building must once have had a connection with the powder mills.

In 1987 I visited the site, further upstream than was previously accessible, to see what had been discovered. Some of the structures had been cleaned off and stabilised, while others had been left untouched. The works were spread over a huge area, and any significant interpretation of the remains would require considerable research. What was evident, however, was the degree to which the river had been harnessed by channels in parallel, rather than in series. Yet again, this was an indication that the flow in the River Darent in the 18th and 19th centuries must have been vastly greater than it has been in modern times.

Lower Paper Mill, Dartford

The water arrangements for this mill site remain, but the mill itself has long gone. It seems to have been a second paper mill, erected in the mid 17th century, some sixty years after John Spilman's famous mill a short distance upstream. It closed in 1790,[68] became a zinc rolling mill for a short time, and was then used for printing silk and calico.

Victoria Mill, Dartford

(See also p.85)

From where the Dartford bypass crosses the River Darent, down to the parish church, the water was split into two separate channels. The west one was basically following the natural river course, but the one to the east was artificial. Each channel powered a mill immediately upstream of the church-side river crossing of the ancient Watling Street. Victoria Mill, also known as Town Mill, Royal Mill, Royal Victoria Mill, Keyes' Mill, Hards' Mill, Daren Mill and, before that, King's Mill, was powered by the eastern channel. The ground floor of the building still survives as the Battle of Britain Memorial Hall, but is only recognisable as a mill when the top of the headrace arch is seen from the southward footpath beside the former watercourse. This arch is actually thirteen feet six inches wide, but only the central, top, part is now visible. The landscape here has been completely changed since I first saw it in 1955.

By that time the mill had already lost its weatherboarded superstructure and only the ground floor remained, the old brickwork disguised by cement render. Span-

Hawley Paper Mill, Sutton-at-Hone. Site of waterwheels. Derek Stoyel, 16th September 1954

Looking upstream at where the pair of low-breast-shot waterwheels used to be. The building on the left is the one seen in the previous photograph, and the blocked circular hole for the wheel-shaft shows up clearly. The smaller blocked hole beyond it, by the bottom corner of the door, marks where the horizontal shaft came out for controlling the water to the wheel. The wider waterwheel to the right used to power a

Opposite bottom: Dartford Powder Mills. One of the incorporating mills. Alan Stoyel, 17th March 1987

Looking downstream at one of the excavated incorporating mills on the east bank of the river, with a second mill beyond on the right. Here the mixed and moistened components of gunpowder were ground to a fine powder by edge runners – pairs of huge millstones which rolled round on their edges upon the face of a third, fixed, horizontal millstone. Each mill comprised two such arrangements, both being driven by one large waterwheel situated between them. This photograph shows the consolidated remains of one of these edge runner arrangements, with the site of the central waterwheel in the foreground. On the river bank are pieces of the huge runner stones, possibly destroyed by one of the explosions which occurred here. None of this was visible in the 1950s.

**Hawley Paper Mill, Sutton-at-Hone. Site of waterwheels. Alan Stoyel,
17th March 1987**

This photograph makes a fascinating comparison with the previous photograph, having been taken from a similar position nearly 33 years later. Almost the only recognisable feature which survives is the scratching of the left-hand brickwork from the narrower waterwheel!

ning an arm of the river, it had water pouring through the wheel-race underneath. Investigation of evidence of the former waterwheel required wading upstream to the tailrace arch, where the gravel bottom had been scoured out deeply by the rushing water. Entering the arch I was surprised to find the water channel running at an angle beneath the building, up to where scratch marks on the wall showed the position of the waterwheel. I found the waterwheel had been low breast-shot, sixteen feet in diameter and approximately eight feet two inches wide, and it had driven gear on the western side of the channel. The top of the breastwork was fitted with an enormous slab of cast-iron. This slab ran the whole width of the wheel and extended down into the deep, rubbish-filled water on the upstream side to an unknown depth, suggesting the former installation of a sliding hatch to control the wheel, as was used by the famous engineer John Rennie. A brick wall separated the wheel-race from the three feet six inches wide bypass channel.

The mill was built in or about 1789 with four pairs of stones at a cost of £2,000,[69] and it ceased work in the 1890s. The waterwheel was wooden with iron floats, driving an iron pitwheel with wooden cogs. The wheel was brought into use again briefly in 1916-17,[70] driving cleaning machinery and a crusher, but it collapsed under the strain and was soon superseded by an electric motor.[71] The upper floors were removed in 1941-2.[72] Old photographs show this to have been a fine, symmetrical building, made resplendent by a large royal coat of arms proudly displayed on it. Its demise could hardly have produced more of a contrast, particularly as the river has now been diverted and canalised to the west, so this sad remnant is now totally separated from its life-source.

Colyer's Mill, Dartford

(See also p.86)

Colyer's Mill, sometimes referred to as Bridge Mill, and later Acacia Hall Mill, occupied an ancient site on the western arm of the River Darent. In September 1954 I called at the mill office nearby and was received courteously by Mr. Donald Strickland, who had worked in the family firm since 1903. R. & H. Strickland had been in the milling business for over a hundred years, and he was kind enough to give me a booklet which had been published to celebrate the firm's centenary in 1951.

Mr. Strickland took me into the large, five-storeyed green weatherboarded building. It had not functioned as a mill since about 1893, and the machinery, including the large iron waterwheel and vertical steam engine, was

completely stripped out in 1898[73] when it was converted into a social club and institute for Burroughs Wellcome & Co.,[74] and was still retained as such. Water could be heard rushing beneath the building, but, frustratingly, there was no means of access, and no opportunity for investigation. There was one feature which was of great interest to me, however. This was the boldly carved inscription "W. PORTER 1808" on a massive beam, and I pondered over its significance. Did it represent the date of construction of the mill? If not, why would anyone leave such incriminating evidence in so prominent a position? Alas, any further on-site investigation is no longer possible; the building was destroyed by fire on 24th January 1962.[75] I returned to the site in 2007, but the whole area in which the mill had stood was now unrecognisable.

Silk Printing Works and Hall's Engineering Works

For me, as a young lad on a bicycle, the busy town of Dartford had little appeal north of Watling Street and the old parish church. I paid one or two casual visits, but I never did any real investigation of water-powered sites below Victoria and Colyer's Mills. This enigmatic area of Dartford had various water-powered industries associated with it at different times. However, apart from the large mill pond which once supplied Phoenix Mills, little evidence now remains.

There was a silk printing works astride a branch of the Darent, a short distance upstream of where the river is crossed by the railway. Sadly I never knew of its existence when I was investigating the local mills, even though it was probably still at work at that time. In about 1986 it was reported as standing derelict, with a concrete water channel clearly leading into it, but the buildings were inaccessible.[76] It was said in 1986 that a waterwheel which

**Opposite bottom:
Victoria Mill, Dartford. Front of mill.
Alan Stoyel, 25th January 1961**

This makes a sad comparison with the previous photograph. It is a similar view, taken from beside the bridge shown in the foreground of the earlier picture. The water is shown rushing out of the tailrace arch of the now-rendered brickwork. Since then, even the water has been diverted right away from the building, so that few passers-by probably even realise that this sad remnant was once such a proud mill.

Victoria Mill, Dartford. Front of mill. E.C. Youens, c.1890s

This fine photograph shows what an impressive and well-proportioned example of a late 18th century mill it was, taken when trade was at its peak. Sporting the royal coat of arms, it demonstrates its royal patronage, and also advertises Daren bread – a local speciality. This is the view from downstream, looking southeast.

Colyers Mill, Dartford. From upstream. Derek Stoyel, 16th September 1954

The mill had long been a social club for Burroughs Wellcome & Co. It was well cared-for, and still retained much character, contributing greatly to a rural oasis in the centre of the town. Viewed from upstream, the waterwheel-house is visible on the left of the mill and the square steam engine chimney is on the right. Nothing is now left of any of this. The mill has gone, a new channel has been cut for the river, and the whole area is now unrecognisable.

had been used for washing the silk here had only recently been broken up during a clearance programme of this section of the river.[77]

A tributary of the Darent, the Cranpit, which flows through Dartford, was once utilised for power by John Hall, the famous millwright who established the engineering empire of J. & E. Hall Ltd. In 1801 he obtained permission to carry out the necessary work involved in the erection of a waterwheel, replacing a windmill, to power some of the machinery in his workshops at Waterside, Hythe Street.[78] In 1802 he insured his millwright's workshop, iron foundry and other buildings, including an iron water wheel.[79] However, any evidence for this use of water power disappeared long ago.

Phoenix Mills, Dartford

(See also p.87)

Not only did Phoenix Mills occupy the last water-pow-

ered site on the river, they were in a different league from all the other Darent mills. The scale and grandeur of the buildings, and the mill-pond in front of it, shouted of industrial might and money. Through the railings I would watch the ducks on the pond, and speculate where the waterways ran under the range of buildings. To a boy the whole place seemed to be unrelated to the smaller rural mills which had such a magnetic appeal, and I never entered the premises. This site formed the barrier against the tidal waters flowing up Dartford Creek from the Thames estuary. Formerly much of the traffic to and from Phoenix Mills was by water and the complex was just as impressive when viewed from the tidal, downstream, side.

The site has had a long and chequered industrial history. It seems to have supported two generations of ironworks from as early as 1590 until a saw-mill replaced it. A technical description of Dartford Sawmill, first published in 1852,[80] was taken from George Rennie's publication of the experience of his father John Rennie (1761-1821), and could be referring to the sawmill on this site, which existed from 1779 until 1790. This sawmill, which had 34 reciprocal saws driven by a waterwheel 16 feet diameter by 4 feet 6 inches wide.[81] Driving such a large number of saws, the power required must have been considerable. The waterwheel was effectivelyy undershot, with a quoted fall of only 2 feet 3 inches, so the volume of water needed could only have been obtained from the main River Darent. The sawmill was superseded by the erection of a large cotton mill in 1790,[82] but this was burnt down in 1795. It then became a steam- and water-powered complex, with two waterwheels,[83] carrying out corn milling and seed crushing. This yielded flour, oil, mustard and various associated products, and claimed to have been the largest of its kind in the kingdom.

The mills burnt down again in 1852 and were largely rebuilt as a huge, mechanised paper mill.[84] The rag engines here were driven by a very powerful breast wheel, eighteen feet in diameter and eighteen feet wide.[85] This phase seems to have ended by 1888, as part of the mill was purchased in that year by Burroughs Wellcome.[86] Another part of the mill was taken over by Mr. Keyes, the miller of Victoria Mill, and he had a Henry Simon roller plant of 4-sacks per hour capacity installed here in 1892.[87] The building was later gutted and the complex was remodelled as a laboratory for Burroughs Wellcome.

Here was a fascinating and enigmatic site at the end of a well-used river system. This was an industrial complex on a huge scale, embracing a succession of industries. Originally based on water power alone, its machinery demanded more than the Darent could provide and, from an early date, powerful steam engines were installed. The site was so good that Phoenix Mills rose from the ashes on more than one occasion. Built at the tidal limit, goods could be brought in and taken away by boat. Here was an economy of scale which could devastate local competition. This complex was the antithesis of the rural mills further upstream and it epitomised the threat which was to force their demise.

Phoenix Mills, Dartford, from downstream. Derek Stoyel 14th September 1969

This is the side of Phoenix Mills which is rarely seen, viewed from the tidal creek downstream of the mills. Only part of the complex is visible here, and much rebuilding has taken place over generations. On the left is the massive circular chimney, a sign of the eventual inability of the River Darent to cope with supplying enough power to the expanding industries it had first attracted to its banks.

National Grid References of sites

River Cray

Orpington Mill, Orpington TQ467669

Snelling's Mill, St. Mary Cray TQ472677

Upper Paper Mill, St. Mary Cray TQ472682

Joynson's Paper Mill, St. Mary Cray TQ471684

Nash's Paper Mill, St. Paul's Cray TQ474694

Foots Cray Paper Mill, Foots Cray TQ475710

Old Mill, Bexley TQ496735

Hall Place Mill, Bexley TQ502743

Evans's Printing Works, Crayford TQ511747

Galbraith's Printing Works, Crayford TQ514747

Swaisland's Printing Works, Crayford TQ517748

Barnes Cray Printing Works, Crayford TQ524749

Crayford Flour Mill, Crayford TQ528755

River Darent

Spring Shaw Mill, Westerham TQ447532

Elm View Mill, Westerham TQ444537

Darenth Mill, Westerham TQ449540

Valence Water Pump, Brasted TQ461535

Mill Farm Mill, Brasted TQ468554

Brasted Mill, Brasted TQ470552

Sundridge Paper Mill, Sundridge TQ489556

Chipstead Mill, Chevening TQ499560

Longford Mill, Otford TQ513568

Whitley Mill, Chevening TQ508533

Bradbourne Mill, Sevenoaks TQ520564

Greatness Corn Mill, Sevenoaks TQ535568

Greatness Silk Mill, Sevenoaks TQ535570

Childs Bridge Mill, Kemsing TQ545580

Longlodge Mill, Otford TQ531584

Otford Mill, Otford TQ524594

Shoreham Corn Mill, Shoreham TQ520610

Glossary

BEDSTONE The lower, fixed, millstone of a pair.

BEVEL GEAR A gear with its face at an angle; used for turning the drive through 90 degrees.

BREAST-SHOT A waterwheel for which the water supply is approximately level with the wheel-shaft. The escape of water is delayed by curved breast-work, of brick, stone, wood or iron, against the lower part of the wheel.

BUCKETS The wooden or iron pockets specifically designed to contain water at the periphery of an overshot or breast-shot waterwheel.

COG A projecting unit on a gear which has been inserted into the wheel; usually made of wood (cf. tooth).

COMPASS ARMED A wheel in which the arms are radial, each arm passing through the mortised shaft.

COMPOSITION STONE A manufactured millstone produced from a cemented mixture of abrasive substances.

CRANK An arm attached to, and rotated by, a shaft, producing an eccentric motion.

CRANKSHAFT A rotating shaft incorporating one or more cranks.

CROSS-TAILED GUDGEON An iron insert with four projecting wings, set in a mortise in the end of a wooden shaft, which is then secured by stout iron rings. The projecting iron pintle is carried in a bearing, allowing the shaft to rotate freely.

CROWN-WHEEL The gear at the top of the upright shaft which drives the ancillary machinery.

DAMSEL An upward extension from the spindle. It agitates the shoe, causing grain to be admitted to the millstones.

FLOATS The projecting parts of a waterwheel upon which the water acts, but is not contained (cf. buckets).

FRENCH BURR A millstone which is made up of numerous cut blocks of flint-like material, quarried in France and imported. The blocks were usually made up into millstones in England.

FULLING MILL A mill used for pounding cloth to give it a felt-like texture.

HEAD The height of the level of impounded water which is available to power a waterwheel or turbine.

HEAD-RACE The channel leading water to a waterwheel.

HOPPER The container, supported by the horse, from which grain is fed via the shoe into the eye of the runner stone.

HORSE The frame standing on the tun and supporting the hopper.

LAYSHAFT A horizontal shaft in a train of gears.

LEAT An artificial watercourse, particularly one leading water to a mill.

LOUVRES A parallel series of boards with gaps between them for ventilation. Often boards can be rotated in series in order to alter air flow.

LOW BREAST-SHOT A waterwheel to which the water enters below shaft level, and there is some curved breastwork, of brick, stone, wood or iron, to delay the escape of the water.

LUCOMB The wooden projection from the loft of a mill into which material can be hoisted directly from a wagon or boat.

MANSARD ROOF A roof which has two pitches, the upper part being at a shallower pitch than the lower part.

MEAL The product of grinding with millstones, before any separation and grading into constituents is carried out.

MEAL FLOOR The floor where the meal from the stones is collected and bagged up. Generally the ground floor in a watermill.

MORTISE WHEEL A gear-wheel with mortises in it to hold wooden cogs. The term is usually applied to a cast-iron wheel.

PEAK A millstone, quarried as a single piece, of Millstone Grit from Derbyshire or Yorkshire.

PENSTOCK The sluice which controls the flow of water to a waterwheel.

PENTROUGH The trough feeding a waterwheel, normally fitted with a penstock.

PIT-WHEEL The main driving gear on the wheel-shaft.

OVERSHOT A waterwheel in which the water is directed onto the top of the wheel in the same direction as it is flowing.

PINION The smaller gear of a pair.

RING GEAR A toothed ring attached to the side of a waterwheel for the purpose of driving machinery.

ROLLER MILL The use of steel rollers to grind the grain; the successor to millstones.

RUNNER STONE The upper millstone which rotates over the fixed bedstone.

SHOE The oscillating tray, shaken by being spring-held against the damsel, feeding grain to the millstones from the hopper.

SHROUDS The continuous flat peripheral surface, of iron or wood, forming the ends of the buckets or floats of a waterwheel, preventing the sideways escape of water.

SLIDING HATCH A form of sluice which is lowered to allow water to run over the top, instead of being raised to let water run beneath it. It is a method of making maximum use of the available head.

SPINDLE The vertical iron shaft supporting and turning the runner stone.

SPUR GEAR A gear in which the cogs or teeth project radially from the rim. These engage similar cogs or teeth on a second gear, the two gears being mounted on parallel shafts.

SPUR-WHEEL A gear in which the cogs or teeth project radially from the rim. The term is used specifically for the large horizontal gear on the upright shaft which engages the stone nuts.

STONE FLOOR The floor on which the millstones are set. Generally the first floor in a watermill.

STONE FURNITURE The fittings associated with millstones, comprising tuns, horses, hoppers and any other related items.

STONE NUT The final pinion in a gear chain in a corn mill. In watermills it is generally mounted on a spindle below the millstones.

SWEEP ROD An arm connected to a crank, converting the circular motion to a reciprocating one.

TAIL-RACE The channel leading water away from a waterwheel.

TOOTH A projecting unit on a wholly iron gear, cast integrally with the wheel or rack (cf. cog).

TUN The casing, usually wooden, which surrounds a pair of millstones.

TURBINE A smaller, highly engineered type of cased waterwheel, specifically designed for particular heads and flows. It rotates much faster, and operates more efficiently, under the specified conditions.

UPRIGHT SHAFT The shaft taking the drive up the mill from the pitwheel (via the wallower). It generally carries a spur-wheel to drive the stones, and a crown-wheel at the top to drive the ancillary machinery.

WALLOWER The gear driven by the pit-wheel at the lower end of the upright shaft.

WHEEL-RACE The water channel in which a breast-shot or undershot waterwheel rotates.

WHEELPIT The pit containing a waterwheel – usually of the overshot type.

WHEEL-SHAFT The horizontal driving shaft on which the waterwheel is mounted.

(Endnotes)

1   Traditionally 'Kentish men' were born west of the River Medway, whereas 'men of Kent' were born east of it.

2   Street, P.E.W., personal notes.

3   Snelling, Miss Lillian, verbal information, 18.5.1954.

4   Street, P.E.W., personal notes.

5   Snelling, Miss Lillian, personal notes.

6   Street, P.E.W., MS notes on "The Rookery", St. Mary Cray, 26.8.1936.

7   Gen. Letter 17.1.1834 (per H.E.S. Simmons)

8   Eldridge, Arthur, verbal information, 21.10.1958.

9   Harris, John, *The History of Kent,* 1719.

10 Shorter, Alfred H., *Paper Mills and Paper Makers in England 1495-1800,* 1957, p.183.

11 *Kentish Times,* 1.11.1929.

12 Box, Thomas, *A practical treatise on Mill-Gearing,* (2nd edition), 1877, pp.148-9 and Figs.54 &55.

13 Stoyel, B.D. & A.J., "The Old Mill Bexley", *Archaeologia Cantiana,* Vol. LXXXIII, 1968, pp.105-110.

14 *Kentish Times,* 6.2.1931 (per H.E.S. Simmons)

15 Hammond, E., verbal information, 6.8.1967.

16 *Sidcup & Kentish Times,* 13.5.1966 & 20.5.1966.

17 Buckland, F., verbal information, 10.1.1953.

18 Buckland, F., MS. History of Bexley.

19 Carr, William, *The Spot that is called Crayford,* 1951, p.90.

20 Greenwood's map of Kent, 1821.

21 Greenwood's map of Kent, 1821.

22 Lambarde, William, *A Perambulation of Kent,* 1570.

23 Carr, William, *The Spot that is called Crayford,* 1951, p.97.

24 This agrees with the statement that the mill had been built about 1820: *Milling,* 6 Dec. 1909.

25 The 5 pairs of stones are corroborated in *The Miller,* 3 Jan. 1887.

26 Verbal information from elderly mill employee, 14.4.1954.

27 Dickinson, H.W., *Water Supply of GreaterLondon,* 1954, p.98.

28 Melville's *Directory of Kent,* 1858

29 Catalogue for sale of mill, 15.6.1891 (per C.P. Davies).

30 *The Miller,* 2.7.1906 (per H.E.S. Simmons).

31 Cumming, Robert F., "Watermills of the River Darent and its Tributaries", MS., c.1992.

32 Kent Archives Office, Maidstone, U120 T128.

33 Dunlop, Sir John, *The Pleasant Town of Sevenoaks,* 1964, pp.140-1.

34 Harrison, Joseph, "Ode on the Silk Mills at Greatness", a 500-line poem, privately printed, 1869.

35 Pearce, Bertram W., *Archaeologia Cantiana,* Vol. XXXLX, 1927, pp.156-7.

36 Stoyel, A.D., "Watermill Sites at Kemsing and Otford", *Archaeologia Cantiana,* Vol.LXXXI, 1966, pp.244-5.

37 Ward notebooks, Otford 2, p.4 et seq., Sevenoaks Library (per A.D. Stoyel)

38 Lot 2, Particulars of sale, 27th Nov. 1837 of property under will of late James Martyr. (per A.D. Stoyel)

39 Cobbs News, property paper, March/April 1985.

40 Fry, C.B., *Life Worth Living,* 1939.

41 *Sevenoaks News,* 3rd June 1954.

42 *South East Gazette,* 6th September 1853 (per C.P. Davies).

43 Rogers, Philip, *A Vale in Kent,* 1955, p.12

44 Simmons, H.E.S., Science Museum colln.

45 Smith, Carlton Alfred, "Sunday Morning, Eynsford, Kent", *Country Life*, 22. 10.1993, p.32.

46 Newspaper cutting (unprovenanced), C.P. Davies colln., Templeman Library, Canterbury.

47 Advertisement, *The Miller*, 23.9.1882 (per H.E.S. Simmons).

48 Booklet: "Centenary of the firm R. & H. Strickland, Dartford, Kent August 1851- August 1951"

49 Cumming, Robert F., "Watermills in Kent – a brief gazetteer" MS., c.1992.

50 Verbal information from elderly man on site, 11.9.1954.

51 Harrison, P.M.J., "The Early Watermills" MS, no date.

52 Hammond, E., verbal information, 22.12.1954.

53 Harrison, P.M.J., personal letter, 29.11.1979.

54 Millen, Walter G., personal letter, 1955.

55 Cumming, Robert F., "Watermills in Kent – a brief gazetteer" MS., c.1992.

56 Rogers, Philip, *A Vale in Kent*, 1955, pp. VII & 108.

57 Cumming, Robert F., "Watermills of the River Darent and its Tributaries", MS., c.1992.

58 Harrison, P.M.J., personal letter, 16.9.1982.

59 Verbal information from elderly local inhabitants, 21.9.1954.

60 Kelly's *Directory of Kent*, 1887, 1890, 1895, 1899 & 1903.

61 Harrison, P.M.J., personal letter, 16.9.1982.

62 Harrison, P.M.J., "The Early Watermills" MS, 4pp., no date, p.1.

63 Keyes, S.K., *Dartford Historical Notes*, 1933.

64 Verbal information from elderly local resident, 1955.

65 Street, P.E.W., personal letter, 10.2.1957.

66 Grove L.R.A., "Inventory of a Sutton-at-Hone Paper Mill in 1710", *Archaeologia Cantiana*, Vol. LXXII, 1958, p.230.

67 Tagg A.C., "The Early History of Paper-making in Dartford", *Trans. Dartford District Antiquarian* Society, No.1, Dec. 1931, p.64.

68 Keyes, S.K., *Further Historical Notes*, 1938, p.476.

69 Keyes, S.K., *Historical Notes*, 1933

70 Verbal information from Mr. Donald Strickland, Jan. 1955.

71 Booklet - "Centenary of the firm of R. & H. Strickland, Dartford, Kent August 1851 – August 1951"

72 *Archaeologia Cantiana*, Vol. LV, 1942.

73 *The Miller*, 5.9.1898 (per H.E.S. Simmons)

74 Keyes, S.K., *Dartford Historical Notes*, 1933.

75 *Dartford Chronicle*, Jan. 1962.

76 Cumming, Robert F., personal communication, 2008.

77 Cumming, Robert F., personal communication, 1986 (information from Bob Barnes)

78 Hesketh, Everard, *J. & E. Hall Ltd. 1785 to 1935*, 1935, pp. 2-3.

79 Royal Exchange Fire Insurance Policy No. 192541, 28 July 1802 (per H.E.S. Simmons).

80 Glynn, Joseph, *The Rudimentary Treatise on the Power of Water* (etc.), 2nd edition, 1875, p.76. [1st edition published in 1852]

81 Glynn, Joseph, *The Rudimentary Treatise on the Power of Water* (etc.), 2nd edition, 1875, p.75.

82 Keyes, S.K., *Dartford Historical Notes*, 1933.

83 Hesketh, E., *J. & E. Hall Ltd. 1785 to 1935*, 1935, p.22.

84 Simmons, H.E.S., Science Museum colln.

85 Box, T, *A Practical Treatise on Mill-Gearing (etc.)*, 1877, p.111 & Fig.56.

86 Keyes, S.K., *Dartford Historical Notes*, 1933.

87 *Milling*, Vol.40, 14.6.1913, p.669.

Index